GemsTV Guide to

Gavin Linsell

At GemsTV we sell our own handcrafted gemstone jewelry and jewelry purchased from our outsource partners directly to customers primarily via television using a "reverse auction" system. Our vertically integrated structure removes the complex supply chains that are traditionally present in the jewelry industry, allowing us to provide better value to customers. Employing over 2,000 people worldwide, Gems TV Holdings Limited is a publicly listed company trading on the Singapore Stock Exchange under the symbol GEMS.

GemsTV currently operates its business through several subsidiaries and a partnership in Germany (**www.GemsTV.de**). We have a manufacturing subsidiary in Thailand, one of the world's leading centers for processing gemstones, and television home shopping subsidiaries in the US (DIRECTV 233) and the UK (Sky Guide 646 & 660 and Virgin TV 755 & 756). Our jewelry is also available on our websites, **www.GemsTV.com** and **www.GemsTV.co.uk**.

In 2005 and 2006, we sold jewelry containing over 170 different gemstone varieties that originated from over 45 countries. Every piece of jewelry we manufacture is handcrafted by our production-line artisans and jewelry specialists.

To obtain a complete bibliography of the books, journals and websites referenced while writing this book, please email **customerservice@GemsTV.com**. For more information and the latest updates on the colorful world of gemstones, please visit **www.GemsTV.com**.

Published by Gems TV Holdings Limited
Printed in Taiwan
ISBN: 978-0-9551491-2-2

FOREWORD

Eight years ago I met a man who changed my life in a colorful way. That man was Don "The Gem Hunter" Kogen and the word "colorful" applies to him in many ways. Apart from a larger than life personality, his passion for gemstones is all about color.

But my first experience handling gems was anything but illustrious – I shot a Topaz from my tweezers several feet, almost taking out Don's eye! Thankfully, I didn't and six years later we launched GemsTV in the UK. Two years on, GemsTV is now broadcasting live in Germany and the US.

While most people think "Diamonds" when they think gemstones, Diamond's popularity is a fairly recent phenomenon. In centuries gone by, it was primarily colored gemstones that adorned royalty, the rich and the famous. Offering a dazzling array of over 170 different gem types from over 45 countries, GemsTV is proud to continue this tradition.

Most people are amazed to learn that this guide was developed in-house. While the task of writing fell on my shoulders, I certainly can't take all the credit. Without the help of people like Jo Wheeler & Praniti Sonsa (graphic designers) and Alex Sharp & Hathaichanok Malee (photographers), this guide wouldn't have happened (a list of all who contributed is included on the last page). Also, if the beginning of wisdom is to call things by their right names, our presenters are the real "gems" at GemsTV. True experts themselves, all have graduated from our rigorous Gems Academy and some have even visited gem mines around the globe.

Apart from gemology, this guide also includes gem legends and lore. When you read about some of the metaphysical properties attributed to gems, please remember that little scientific evidence exists to substantiate these beliefs.

With a plethora of different gemstones featured on GemsTV, 365 days a year, this guide provides reliable information on our main varieties. While we can't guarantee we'll always have all the gems featured in this guide, part of their charm is that you're never sure what surprises the next gem hunt will unearth…

Best wishes,

Gavin Linsell
May 2007

CONTENTS

A-Z OF GEMS CONTENTS

As gemstones are sometimes referred to by different names, if you can't find the gem you're looking for on this page, please use the index on page 221.

Alternatively, please check the list on page 157 for gem varieties whose information can be found on **www.GemsTV.com**.

Please note that the origins provided in the tables for each gem type are the countries from which GemsTV currently sources these gems.

AGATE

Agate is the banded form of Chalcedony (also spelled Calcedony and correctly pronounced as "Kal-ced-on-ee," it is the catchall term for cryptocrystalline Quartz) and its name was derived from the site of its discovery, the river Achates (now Dirillo) in southwest Sicily. You will often find beautifully flowing patterns within Agate, which are caused by the presence of iron and manganese.

Legends and lore

Said by the ancients to render the wearer invisible, Agate has been admired by humanity for thousands of years. Its beauty and durability have prompted humankind to use it for both practical and ornamental purposes. Valued by the ancient Sumerians and Egyptians who used it for amulets and ornamental pieces, Agate is one of the oldest known gems. In Roman times, Agate intaglio (a gem carved in negative relief) signet rings were particularly popular.

Fire Agate 14K Yellow Gold Ring

Agate is mentioned in the Bible as being one of the "stones of fire" (Ezekiel 28:13-16) that were given to Moses and set in the breastplate of Aaron (Exodus 28:15-30). A variety of Agate, Sardonyx is one of the twelve gemstones set in the foundations of the city walls of Jerusalem (Revelations 21:19). As compiled by Andreas, Bishop of Caesurae, one of the earliest writers to tie the Apostles with the symbolism of the twelve gems of Jerusalem, Sardonyx represents the Apostle James. Agate was especially valued during medieval times when one of the more outlandish uses was to bind an Agate to each horn of an ox to ensure a good harvest. The danger here is that your Agated beasts of burden may then become invisible and a little hard to find! Agate is believed to cure insomnia, ensure pleasant dreams, protect against danger and promote strength and healing.

Just the facts

The main conditions necessary for Agate formation are the presence of silica from devitrified volcanic ash, water from rainfall or ground sources, manganese, iron and other mineral oxides that form the white, red, blue, gray, brown or black bands. Agate comes in many different forms ranging from transparent to opaque. Varieties include Blue Agate, Blue Lace Agate, Crazy Lace Agate, Green Agate, Indian Agate, Moss Agate, Fire Agate, Tree Agate, Onyx, Sardonyx and Wood Agate.

Agate showing colorful bands

AGATE:	Mentioned in the Bible
Origins:	Brazil, India & South Africa
Colors Found:	Various
Family:	Chalcedony Quartz
Hardness:	6.50 - 7.00
Refractive Index:	1.53 - 1.54
Relative Density:	2.55 - 2.64

ALEXANDRITE

Known in Russia as the "gem of the tsars," color change Alexandrite is truly a miraculous gemstone. Often described as "Emerald by day" and "Ruby by night," when viewed under sunlight Alexandrite appears teal to forest green, but when seen by candlelight, it appears violet, crimson red, raspberry, purple or orange.

Scant availability, remarkable color change, excellent durability and a sparkling "adamantine" or Diamond-like luster, makes Alexandrite a "must have" for any true jewelry connoisseur. A rare variety of Chrysoberyl, Alexandrite ranks alongside Tanzanite and Padparadscha Sapphire as one of the world's most coveted gemstones.

Legends and lore

Early one chilly October morning in 1830, a Russian peasant charcoal burner, Maxim Stefanovitch Koshevnikov, was making his way through the silver birch forests along the banks of the Tokovaya River. Tripping on the exposed roots of a large tree felled by a storm, he discovered some green gemstones. Quickly identified as Emeralds, by 1831 this deposit in Russia's Ural Mountains was being mined.

Alexandrite & Diamond
18K Yellow Gold Ring

The Tokovaya Emerald mines also yielded other gemstones, including a new one that had the strange ability to change color. When viewed under sunlight, rich green colors appeared but when seen by candlelight it displayed red hues. The gem was named "Alexandrite" after the young Tsarevitch, who was crowned Tsar Alexander II in 1855. Legend has it that Alexandrite was discovered by Emerald miners on his birthday, April 23, 1830, the year the Russian heir apparent came of age. As the date of the deposit's discovery and the alleged naming of the gem conflict, Vitaliy Repej, a Ukrainian Alexandrite specialist, instead believes that Alexandrite was actually discovered on April 3, 1834, by the Tsar's famous Finnish mineralogist Dr. Nils Nordenskjold and wasn't officially called Alexandrite until 1842.

Alexandrite in different lighting conditions
displaying its characteristic color change

Its birthday aside, this new gem created a sensation - everyone wanted an Alexandrite! But this was certainly no fun for the miners. Following the sparse Alexandrite veins through pegmatite rock with hand dug trenches, open pits and small tunnels, mining was very primitive to say the least. Imagine working through long winters plagued by biting cold and blinding snowdrifts. Summer brought no respite, just great swarms of gnats, mosquitoes and gadflies.

ALEXANDRITE

The discovery of Alexandrite on the future Tsar's birthday was considered especially fortunate as the colors displayed by this unusual gem can mirror the Imperial Russian military colors of red and green. Possessing nationalistic connotations, Alexandrite quickly gained popularity in Russia, where it was believed to bring good luck.

Because of its two colors, in Russia it is also believed to invite loneliness if you only wear one piece of Alexandrite jewelry.

Alexandrite is believed by crystal healers to strengthen the wearer's intuition in critical situations. Some also attribute Alexandrite with the ability to aid creativity and inspire imagination.

Just the facts

In gemology, any Chrysoberyl that changes color can be called Alexandrite. The nomenclature is not dependent on the colors of the change. However, Alexandrite's color change is dependent on pure light sources (pure candescent light to pure incandescent light, for example sunlight to candlelight).

Interestingly, the color change effect is not unique to Alexandrite. Many gem types display color change, such as Sapphire and Garnet. However, the degree of color change exhibited by Alexandrite is the most extreme encountered in natural gems.

Similar to Emeralds, inclusions are a common feature in Alexandrite. Far from being flaws, inclusions record a gem's natural relationship with the earth. Given the prevalence of synthetic Alexandrite, they are also a fascinating hallmark of authenticity that helps us distinguish real gems from artificial impostors.

*Alexandrite & Diamond 18K Yellow Gold Ring
showing its ability to change color
in different light sources*

Arguably, one of the best uses of Alexandrite is in earrings and pendants. In this position, the vibrancy of Alexandrite's color change is easily noticed. Alexandrite rings are also popular, as it is a very tough gem with a hardness that is only transcended by Rubies, Sapphires or Diamonds.

Because of this gem's scarcity, Alexandrite is found in a wide variety of shapes and sizes faceted to maximize the carat weight and beauty of each individual crystal.

Coveted for its beautiful and mysterious optical effects, when you look at a Cat's Eye Alexandrite you can see a single band of light on its surface. Technically known as "chatoyancy," this intriguing phenomenon is unique to the world of gemstones. It

Alexandrite & Diamond 18K White Gold Ring

ALEXANDRITE

Alexandrite 14K Yellow Gold Bracelet

Alexandrite & Diamond 18K Yellow Gold Pendant

ALEXANDRITE:	June's birthstone
Origins:	India, Madagascar & Tanzania
Colors Found:	Teal, blue green to forest green changing to violet, crimson red, raspberry, purple & orange
Family:	Chrysoberyl
Hardness:	8.50
Refractive Index:	1.74 - 1.75
Relative Density:	3.71

is caused by minerals reflecting a band of light back to the eye like a mirror. Cat's Eye Alexandrite makes particularly stunning signet rings and is a powerful display of a unique sense of style.

While beautiful Alexandrite is available from other locales, among Alexandrite connoisseurs, Russian Alexandrite maintains an historical pedigree that is highly coveted. In 1898 Edwin Streeter wrote in "Precious Stones & Gems": "The wonderful Alexandrite is an Emerald by day and an Amethyst at night. Its market value is extremely variable and sometimes as much as £20 per carat is paid for a fine stone." Today, the same Russian Alexandrite is worth many thousands of dollars!

Although the Tokovaya deposit closed after only a few decades, limited mining is rumored to have resumed around 1995. To date, very little mining of Russian Alexandrite is taking place. In December 2005, "Colored Stone" reported that "there have been unconfirmed reports of new activity in this area, but no significant amount of material has hit the market yet." While it is a country rich in gemstones, since the fall of the Soviet Union much of Russia's gems have not been mined due to both economic conditions and outdated mining practices. Interestingly, both De Beers (a famed Diamond consortium) and Russian geologists are currently surveying Russian Diamond reserves and an offshoot of this exploration may be the discovery of new Alexandrite deposits. Regardless, very little Russian Alexandrite is available and those lucky enough to own one truly are custodians of a gem from a bygone era.

While it wasn't until 1996 that the tribal peoples of Andhra Pradesh unearthed the first hints of Alexandrite in the Araku Valley, since its discovery Indian Alexandrite has endured a history as turbulent as Imperial Russia. From much needed mining regulation in 1999, to the destruction of coastal mines during the 2004 tsunami, Indian Alexandrite has certainly had its ups and downs. Displaying teal apple greens with changes ranging from orange raspberries to grape, the first Alexandrite ever featured on GemsTV was from Vishnakahaputnam in Andhra Pradesh, India. Always on the hunt for this stunning gem, we recently encountered Indian Alexandrite from a new locale whose rich colors are reminiscent of Alexandrite from the original Russian deposit. Today, Indian Alexandrite primarily hails from Narsipattnanm, 62 miles inland from the first discovery in Vishnakahaputnam. It is characterized by

ALEXANDRITE

an intense green with an incredible color change that ranges from vibrant Amethyst, to Ruby red and reddish purple. Formed hundreds of millions of years ago during the Paleozoic era, it is believed that the pegmatite rocks found at the location of Alexandrite's discovery in the Urals in Russia and at Narsipattnanm are the same. Mining Indian Alexandrite is a dangerous business and the tribal miners risk life and limb tunneling muddy soil to a depth of 98 feet to find rocks rich with tiny clusters of Alexandrite.

While gems from the famous Brazilian state of Minas Gerais have enchanted the world for over 100 years, good quality Alexandrite was only discovered in 1987. As with other mines containing pegmatite rocks, Brazilian Alexandrite is found in rugged areas that can be difficult to access. Usually mined using primitive hand tools, one of the most famous exceptions is the Hematitia mine, whose beautiful Alexandrite is now regrettably depleted. Although the majority of Brazilian Alexandrite contains many inclusions or is translucent, a tiny amount of better quality gems has been unearthed. In 2004, a new pocket of Brazilian Alexandrite was discovered, yielding blue green Alexandrite that changed to a delightful raspberry red.

Mines in Madagascar, Tanzania and Mozambique, have been producing good quality Alexandrite for several years. African Alexandrite is typically located in wet regions near rivers and mined by digging through river beds by hand to unearth the Alexandrite-rich pegmatite rock.

For approximately 90 years Russia and Sri Lanka were the only known sources of Alexandrite. Obtained from alluvial gravels (in contrast to most other deposits that are mined from host pegmatite rock), Sri Lankan Alexandrite is characterized by a fine Sapphire green color in daylight with a change to columbine red, similar to purplish red Spinel, in incandescent light.

AMBER

Amber is the ancient and fossilized resin of long dead trees that grew in forests millions of years ago. Over the eons, chemical and physical changes occurred, fossilizing the resin to produce the Amber we know today.

Research indicates that Amber ranges from about 2 million to 360 million years in age although most gem quality Amber ranges from 5 million to 50 million years.

Amber is a unique gem. In addition to its beauty, Amber bequeaths humankind valuable scientific data through its ability to act as a window on the past. Its unique ability to preserve the organic tissues of prehistoric life forms is valued by both gem collectors and scientists.

Legends and lore

In classical times, Amber was used medicinally and was also believed to offer a magical light for the deceased as they progressed through the underworld. Given this association, Amber was once believed to provide magicians and sorcerers with special powers.

Other attributes associated with Amber include love, strength, luck, healing, protection and the ability to calm stressed nerves.

Amber 14K Yellow Gold Ring

Just the facts

When you rub Amber, static electricity is generated. In fact, the word electricity is derived from the ancient Greek word for Amber, "elektron" or "sun made." Although Amber is a fossilized plant resin that generally consists of organic carbon, hydrogen and oxygen structures, the composition varies depending on the type of parental plant species.

The process and transformation of tree resin into Amber is not fully understood. However, there are several elements which are recognized as being essential, namely molecular polymerization (the combination of many molecules to form a more complex product of higher molecular weight), evaporation of turpenes (volatile oils – volatiles are substances that can be readily vaporized), heat and pressure.

Amber 14K Yellow Gold Pendant

While the rate of transition from tree resin to Amber is often represented as a linear process, in reality it is variable. There are many different types of fossilized tree resin found all over the world. Each deposit has

Amber 14K Yellow Gold Ring

10

AMBER

unique chemical components, but can physically appear almost identical. In some cases, detailed chemical analysis is required to determine geographic origin. Following its secretion tree resin immediately begins to lose its original plasticity and harden. There are several forms of commercially exploited resin including Ambergris, Arabic Gum, Dammar, Frankincense, Gum Lac (sometimes called Shellac), Kauri Gum, Mastic, Myrrh, Rosin and Sandarach.

Copal is a more mature form of resin. The word Copal comes from the Spanish word "copalli," which means incense, an actual use of Copal. Polymerization has now progressed significantly through the body of the resin. In some cases the surface of the Copal has fractured and crazed due to surface shrinkage prompted through the initial evaporation of turpenes, which can also commence during this period. Distinguishing between Copal and Amber is a contentious issue among Amber experts because there is no scaling system for assessing polymerization against age. Even though significant Copal deposits exist in Colombia and South America that are less than 1,000 years old, the process of polymerization may take thousands of years before the resultant material can be called Copal. This is because many external factors affect the rate of molecular linking. The complete transition from resin to Amber needs two additional factors present: heat and pressure. Heat and pressure may support the process of polymerization and turpene evaporation, but their full effect upon the formation of Amber is not completely understood. The length of time needed to reach the point at which the majority of turpenes have escaped varies depending on surrounding conditions and the nature of the resin at the moment of its formation.

The organic inclusions commonly found in Amber include plant debris, small animals and a variety of prehistoric insects. These ancient creatures are predominantly extinct ancestors of today's cockroaches, ants, termites, caddis flies, centipedes, crickets, scorpions and millipedes. These preserved life forms were trapped by fresh sticky resin that oozed from coniferous trees millions of years ago. Preserved in the Amber, the insects are visible in almost perfect condition, showing the position they were in when they were entombed millions of years ago.

Green Amber 14K Yellow Gold Ring

Green Amber & White Topaz 14K Yellow Gold Ring

Green Amber 14K Yellow Gold Ring

11

AMBER

Amber 925 Silver Pendant

Baltic Amber

The most valued variety of Amber for manufacturing jewelry and decorative objects is Baltic Amber. Baltic Amber is also known as Succinite after its parent tree Pinus Succinfera that was common in the Tertiary period, some 50 million years ago. The living tree that is thought to be the most visually similar is Agathis Australis. At present, the primary source of Baltic Amber is the various deposits around the Russian port of Kaliningrad, the old German enclave of Koenigsberg. Annexed from the Germans after WW2, it is located on the southern Baltic coast between Poland and Lithuania. It is also called The Western Russian Enclave or Special Economic Zone "Yantar" (the Russian word for Amber). Below 98 feet of sand around Kaliningrad there is a 30-foot alluvial layer of Amber containing clay called "blue earth." It is mined from the surface in open pits with dredging buckets. The "blue earth" is then washed and the Amber picked out by hand.

Typically yellow, golden or brown, Baltic Amber reportedly comes in 256 documented shades. The color of Amber is influenced by changes in the resin when it is exuded from the tree. For example, Green Amber formed when small parts of plants got in the resin (the green color is a result of plant interaction with the resin).

Incredibly light, Amber is occasionally buoyant in salt water and Baltic Amber is sometimes transported long distances by the sea, having been found as far away as the beaches of England and Scotland. It's from this ability it gains one of its common names, "sea stone." Important secondary sources include the Dominican Republic and Mexico.

Since the Jurassic Park movies, interest in Amber with insect and animal inclusions has exploded, making it highly collectible. In regard to the film "Jurassic Park," the alleged source of the dinosaur DNA was Dominican Amber. However, Dominican Amber is thought to be about 25 million years too young to truly contain dinosaur DNA. However, other Amber sources from around the world could potentially contain the genetic material of these avian ancestors.

In 1994 a molecular biologist from California reported that he had extracted DNA from an insect sealed in Amber 120 to 130 million years ago. Dr. Raul Canu claimed the insect was trapped when dinosaurs ruled the earth, leading people to speculate that Michael Crichton's novel could one day become a scientific reality.

AMBER:	Preserves prehistoric life forms
Origins:	Russia
Colors Found:	Golden yellow, pale yellow, blue, green, deep cherry red to dark brown
Family:	Organics
Hardness:	2.00 - 3.00
Refractive Index:	1.54
Relative Density:	1.05 - 1.10

"An engraved Amethyst bearing the figure of a little Cupid is said to have been worn in a ring by St. Valentine."

George Frederick Kunz

AMETHYST

Amethyst 14K Yellow Gold Ring

Rose de France Amethyst 14K White Gold Ring

Amethyst & White Topaz 14K Yellow Gold Ring

Dionysus, known for his love of grape juice, was the Greek god of wine; however after a few goblets he became a little confrontational. One day in the forest with goblet in hand, the tipsy Dionysus took insult from a passing mortal that refused to show him respect. The incident provoked his wrath and Dionysus swore revenge on the next mortal that he saw…

Along came Amethyst, a beautiful young maiden on her way to pay tribute to the goddess Diana. Dionysus targeted Amethyst as the object of his revenge, and with the snap of his fingers, he summoned two ferocious tigers to devour the girl. As Dionysus sat back to enjoy the spectacle, Amethyst cried out to her goddess Diana. Seeing what was about to happen, Diana transformed Amethyst into a glimmering pure white Quartz statue thus protecting her from the ferocious tigers. Moved with guilt, Dionysus realized the ruthlessness of his actions and began to weep with sorrow. As the tears dripped into his goblet, Dionysus collapsed, spilling the tear-tainted wine onto the statue of Amethyst. The white Quartz absorbed the wine's color creating the colored gem that we refer to today as Amethyst, the gemstone of the gods.

Legends and lore

With the mythology surrounding the origin of Amethyst, it is perhaps fitting that it was once considered a talisman to prevent drunkenness, which explains why wine goblets were once made from this gem. As the ancient Greeks often playfully manipulated words from other languages, it is possible that they jokingly converted the Hebrew word for a purple gem, "achlamath," to the Greek word "amethustos," meaning "not drunk," from which the modern name for Amethyst is derived. In legend, it is usually taken literally, as if the Greeks really thought Amethyst would prevent drunkenness.

Amethyst's shades of purple have served as a symbol of royalty throughout history. Pharaohs, kings and queens, as well as leading lights in religious sects have long treasured it because of its rich, royal color.

Interestingly, this fascination with the color purple dates back to Roman times when generals celebrating triumphs (and later emperors who never fought a battle) got to wear a "toga picta" (a bright purple toga with gold embroidery).

AMETHYST

Because Amethyst was thought to encourage celibacy (it was believed to have a sobering effect not only on drunkards, but also upon those overexcited by passion), Amethyst was very important in the decoration of Catholic churches in the Middle Ages. Considered to be the "papal stone," even today bishops still wear Amethyst rings.

Many other qualities were attributed to Amethyst in the 15th century. Leonardo Da Vinci wrote that Amethyst was able to dissipate evil thoughts and quicken the intelligence. It was also believed to render people shrewd in business matters, preserve soldiers from harm and assist hunters in capturing wild animals.

The history of adornment can be traced back to the Minoan period in Greece (circa 2500 BC), where Amethyst has been found as polished cabochons set into gold rings. Popular in the 19th century, Amethyst was a favorite gem in art nouveau jewelry.

Just the facts

Colored by iron, Amethyst is a variety of macrocrystalline Quartz that occurs in transparent pastel roses to deep purples.

Like many other gemstones, the quality of Amethyst varies according to its source. Amethyst from the Americas can be found in large sizes as opposed to African Amethyst (typically mined in Madagascar and Zambia), which is sometimes small but carries a higher saturation in color. Dark, highly saturated Amethyst is also found in Australia. The now historic Siberian variety is deep purple with occasional red and blue flashes and commands the highest price. However, the most prolific origin is Brazil, and if we were to believe Dionysus' wine was indeed the source of its color, Brazilian Amethyst would have been born from the finest vintages.

First appearing in Europe in 1727, Brazilian Amethyst soon became highly fashionable and expensive. Amethyst was very popular in France and England during the 18th century and many affluent families invested large amounts of money in this gemstone. For example, a necklace of Amethysts was purchased at a very high price for Queen Charlotte (1744-1818), wife of George III of England.

The chief mining areas for Brazilian Amethyst are Minas Gerais, Bahia and Maraba. Neighboring Uruguay offers spectacularly beautiful varieties of

Amethyst 14K White Gold Ring

Uruguayan Amethyst

AMETHYST:	February's birthstone
Origins:	Brazil, Kenya, Madagascar, Uruguay & Zambia
Colors Found:	Pinkish purple to purple
Family:	Quartz
Hardness:	7.00
Refractive Index:	1.54 - 1.55
Relative Density:	6.50

15

AMETHYST

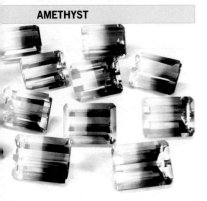

Amethyst that were only discovered a few years ago.

Rose de France Amethyst (also known as Lavender Amethyst) is the name for Brazilian Amethyst of a pastel lilac pinkish hue. Rose de France Amethyst was a very popular Victorian gem and while Rose de France Amethyst frequently appears in antique jewelry, it is currently experiencing a revival in popularity as part of a general awakening to the beauty of pastel gems.

Multi Color Amethyst beautifully melds the regal purple lavenders of Amethyst with the ice whites of White Quartz in one gem. Multi Color Amethyst occurs because of environmental changes during formation. At different times, the color-causing element (iron) was incorporated into the crystal, causing different color layers. Purposely cut to showcase this feature, Multi Color Amethyst is generally judged by the balanced contrast between its colors. Cutting the gem so both colors show is sometimes challenging for cutters. While notoriously difficult to cut consistently, a well cut multicolored gem is a real delight.

AMETRINE

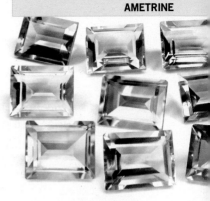

Ametrine is one of the world's most unusual gemstones in that it is actually two gems in one! Multicolor Ametrine blends the golden sunburst of Citrine with the purple sunset of Amethyst.

Legends and lore

Ametrine is said to posses all the metaphysical benefits of both Amethyst and Citrine, as well its own unique properties. Ametrine is said to aid in meditation, relieve tension, disperse negativity and help eliminate prejudice.

Just the facts

The unusual color variation found in Ametrine is due to the presence of iron in different oxidation states within the crystalline structure. Exactly how this occurs is not fully understood.

The world's main source of Ametrine, the Bolivian Anahi Mine became famous in the 17th century when a Spanish Conquistador received it as a dowry after marrying an Ayoreos princess named Anahi.

Ametrine has only been readily available to the consumer market since 1980 when material from the Anahi Mine in Bolivia began to appear in larger quantities. Before this it was considered to be quite unusual and was also known as Amethyst-Citrine Quartz, Trystine or Golden Amethyst.

The color split is usually highlighted by cutting the gem into long shapes ideal for rings, earrings and necklaces. Larger Ametrine gemstones make particularly enchanting pendants, perfect for evening wear.

A fine split in the colors and color intensity are the most important aspects to consider when evaluating Ametrine.

Ametrine is an amazing gemstone with a split personality. When handcrafting Ametrine jewelry we always try to ensure that both the Amethyst and the Citrine are clearly visible to the naked eye.

Ametrine & White Topaz 14K Yellow Gold Ring

Ametrine 14K Yellow Gold Ring

Ametrine

AMETRINE:	Multicolor gem
Origins:	Bolivia
Colors Found:	Golden & purple
Family:	Quartz
Hardness:	7.00
Refractive Index:	1.54 - 1.55
Relative Density:	6.50

AMETRINE

**Ametrine is actually two gems in one. It blends the golden
sunburst of Citrine with the purple sunset of Amethyst.**

Andalusite, an aluminum silicate, derives its name from the site of its discovery, Almeria in the southern Spanish province of Andalusia.

While Andalusite's color play has been compared to Alexandrite, this is technically incorrect, as pleochroic (displaying different colors in different directions) gemstones like Andalusite feature all their colors at once, whereas Alexandrite only changes color in different light sources.

Legends and lore

Some Andalusite crystals have carbonaceous inclusions, arranged so that in cross section they form a dark cross. This variety is called "Chiastolite" (named after the Greek word for cross) and sometimes referred to in ancient texts as "lapis crucifer," meaning "cross stone." Chiastolite is found in schist rock formations near the town of Santiago de Compostela, northwest Spain, and many amulets of the "cross stone" were once sold to pilgrims. Chiastolite is often mentioned as a gemstone of protection and was once used to thwart evil eye curses.

Andalusite is considered by crystal healers to be a gemstone that enhances intellect, problem solving abilities and mental clarity. It is also mentioned as being conducive to the receipt of messages from the netherworld.

Just the facts

Andalusite is a polymorph with two other minerals, Kyanite and Sillimanite. Andalusite typically occurs in thermally metamorphosed pelitic rocks, and in pelites that have been regionally metamorphosed under low-pressure conditions. It also occurs, together with Corundum, Tourmaline, Topaz and other minerals in some pegmatites.

When cutting strongly pleochroic gemstones (Iolite, Tanzanite, Kunzite, etc.), lapidaries typically try to minimize the pleochroism and maximize the single most attractive color. Interestingly, Andalusite is the opposite, as all the colors visible in different directions are attractive. Cutters therefore try to orient the gem to get a pleasing mix of its orange, brown, yellow, green and golden colors. When cut successfully, Andalusite looks unlike any other gemstone, displaying patterns of color dancing around its facets.

ANDALUSITE

Andalusite & White Topaz 14K White Gold Ring

Andalusite

ANDALUSITE:	Pleochroism
Origins:	Brazil, Mozambique & Sri Lanka
Colors Found:	Brown, green, orange, red & white
Family:	Andalusite
Hardness:	4.50 - 7.00
Refractive Index:	1.71 - 1.73
Relative Density:	3.56 - 3.68

19

APATITE

While it sounds like it's hungry, it's actually trying to fool you! The name Apatite comes from the Greek word "apatao," meaning "to deceive," as Apatite has often been confused with gems such as Paraiba Tourmaline, Peridot (Olivine) and Beryl. Ironically, the phosphates in bones and teeth of all vertebrate animals are members of the Apatite group, so the hunger connection is quite appropriate after all!

Legends and lore

Apatite is said to enhance one's insight, learning abilities and creativity, and to give increased self-confidence. It also is said to help achieve deeper states of meditation. Using Apatite is said to facilitate the desired results when working with other crystals. Apatite is also believed by crystal healers to be useful to help improve one's coordination, to strengthen muscles, help suppress hunger and to ease hypertension.

Apatite & White Topaz 14K Yellow Gold Pendant

Just the facts

Apatite is actually three different minerals depending on the predominance of either fluorine, chlorine or the hydroxyl group: calcium (fluoro, chloro, hydroxyl) phosphate. These ions can freely substitute in the crystal lattice and all three are usually present in every specimen although some specimens are almost 100% pure in one group. Gem quality Apatite is rare, particularly over 1 carat. The color of Apatite is often due to the presence of rare earth elements. It comes in many colors, including green, yellow, blue, violet, and a yellow-green variety, originally mined in Spain, commonly called "asparagus stone" because of its similarity in color to the vegetable. Cat's Eye Apatite is also known to exist.

Apatite

Fort Dauphin Apatite

While Apatite wasn't unearthed in Madagascar until 1995, the French began working the Fort Dauphin area in the 1930's after shepherds found some gems. Located in the southeast of Madagascar, practically at the end of the world, Fort Dauphin was established in 1642 and abandoned in 1674 following an 18-month siege by Antanosy tribesmen. It is believed that the famed pirate republic of Libertalia was later established here. The recent finds of Apatite in Madagascar have added to the popularity of this gem. Exhibiting excellent saturation, Madagascan Apatite's colors range from neon "Emerald" greens (as typified by our Fort Dauphin Apatite) to neon "Paraiba" blues.

APATITE:	Pleochroism
Origins:	Brazil, Kenya, Madagascar, Mozambique & Sri Lanka
Colors Found:	Blue, green, violet, yellow & yellow-green
Family:	Apatite
Hardness:	5.00
Refractive Index:	1.63 - 1.64
Relative Density:	3.10 - 3.30

AQUAMARINE

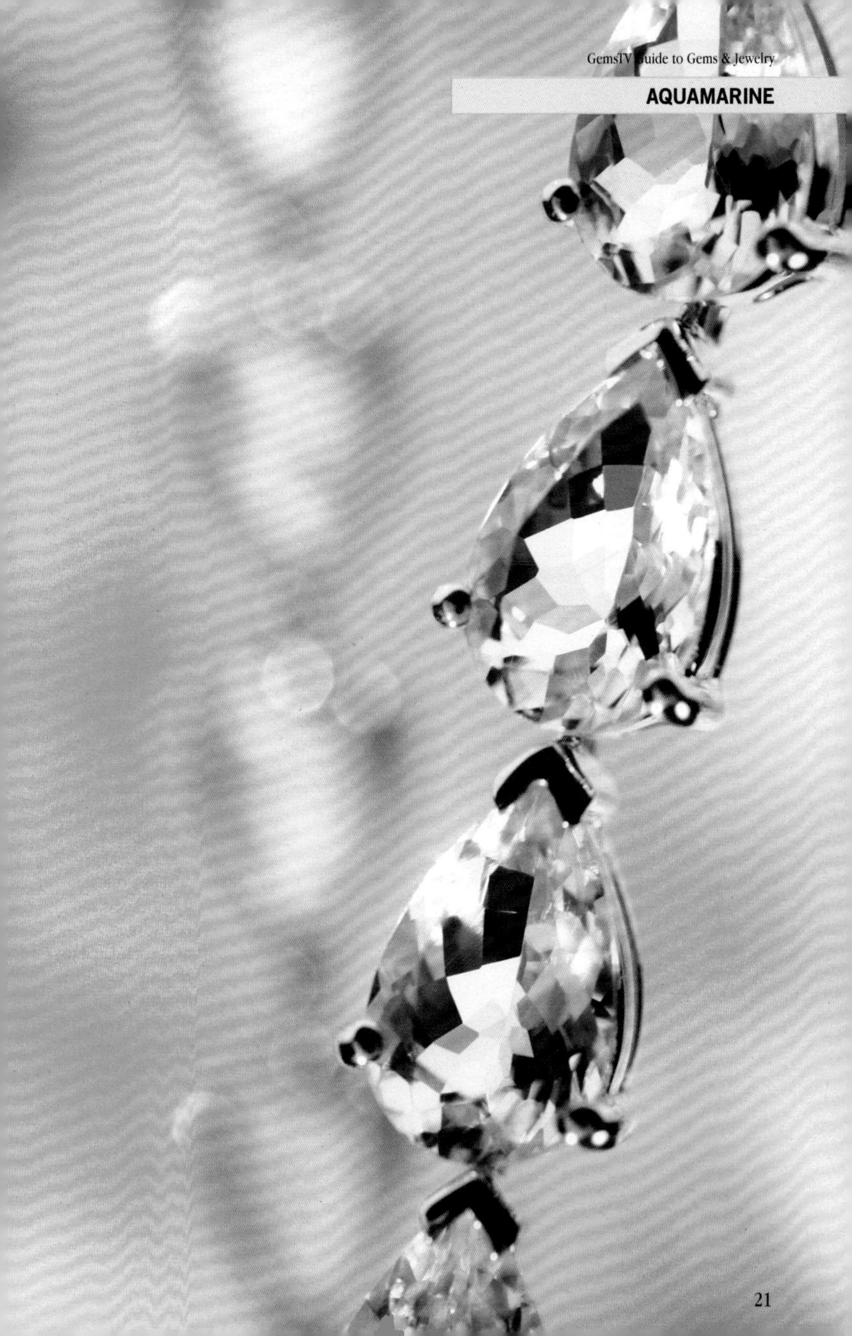

AQUAMARINE

Symbolizing the near perfect clarity and transparency of the ocean, the sheer beauty of Aquamarine, with its wonderful color and fantastic clarity, makes it popular with both the collector and the wearer of fine jewelry. It will come as no surprise that its name was derived from the Latin words for "water of the sea."

Blue, the world's most popular color, is famous for its calming effect, and out of all the blues available none match the serenity found in Aquamarine. Aquamarine embodies all that is natural. Aquamarine, the sparkling birthstone for March, ranges from pastel blue to light green, its tones reminiscent of an invigorating sea breeze.

Legends and lore

Since antiquity, Aquamarine has been seen as a gemstone of great vision, its crystals often being used as eyes in the creation of statues that symbolize power and wisdom. According to legend, any man or woman that set eyes on these statues became a person of great wisdom, harnessing the ability to see into the future. On occasions, these statues were placed in strategic positions near the coastline where they could calm the wrath of the god Poseidon, thus ensuring the safe return of those on ships at sea.

Santa Maria Africana Aquamarine & White Topaz
14K Yellow Gold Ring

Aquamarine has long been associated with its ability to capture oceanic energy. When amulets made of Aquamarine were worn, sailors believed that unmatched bravery would be instilled in their souls. These fishermen's friends accompanied their owners while out on the high seas, and in the event of a storm, were tossed overboard to placate Poseidon's anger. Interestingly, Thai culture contains a common belief that Aquamarine can ward off seasickness and prevent wearers from drowning. Because of its association with the sea, Aquamarine is considered to be a gemstone of purification and cleansing that washes the mind with fresh clear thoughts and promotes self-expression. Its calming effects make it a popular gemstone for those who practice meditation, as it is also believed to eradicate fears and phobias.

Aquamarine

Just the facts

Colored by trace amounts of iron, Aquamarine is a member of the Beryl family whose members also include Bixbite, Goshenite, Emerald, Heliodor and Morganite. The color ranges depending on the

AQUAMARINE:	March's birthstone
Origins:	Brazil, Madagascar, Mozambique, Namibia, Nigeria, Tanzania & Zambia
Colors Found:	Pastel blue to bluish green
Family:	Beryl
Hardness:	7.50 - 8.00
Refractive Index:	1.57 - 1.59
Relative Density:	2.68 - 2.80

AQUAMARINE

relative concentrations and location of iron within the Beryl crystal structure. While noted for its excellent clarity, inclusions are more prevalent (and accepted) in the more intense hues.

Brazil has been the world's major supplier of Aquamarine for decades. The famous Marambaia area is one of the most important sources of fine Aquamarine in the world. Today however, several African nations, including Nigeria, Mozambique, Zambia and Madagascar provide an equal, if not greater supply of similarly beautiful examples. The different shades of Aquamarine are distinguished by their own names. "Santa Maria" is the name of the rare, intensely deep blue Aquamarine found in the Santa Maria de Itabira mines of Brazil. Since 1991, very similar colors have also been found in certain mines in Africa, especially in Mozambique, where they have come to be known as "Santa Maria Africana."

Another Brazilian beauty is the deep blue "Espirito Santo," coming from the Brazilian state of Espirito Santo. Another beautifully colored variety has taken its name from a 1954 Brazilian beauty queen, "Martha Rocha."

Recognized as a gem-producing country since Portuguese colonial times, Mozambique is increasingly becoming more visible in the global gem community, primarily due to its excellent quality Aquamarines. Mozambique governmental poverty eradication policies have been key factors in the development of the mining industry, creating conditions for prospecting projects to take place at a national level.

AVENTURINE

Green Aventurine 14K White Gold Ring

Aventurine

AVENTURINE:	Aventurescence
Origins:	Brazil, India & US
Colors Found:	Blue, brown, creamy green, green & peach
Family:	Quartz
Hardness:	6.50
Refractive Index:	1.54
Relative Density:	2.59 - 2.61

Aventurine's name is derived from an accident. During the 18th century, Venetian glass workers were preparing molten glass when copper filings accidentally fell into the batch, producing glass with sparkles. The name Aventurine comes from the Italian "a ventura" which means "by chance." But make no mistake, Aventurine is certainly not glass, it is actually a much sought after member of the Chalcedony Quartz family.

Legends and lore

Aventurine has been used as a lucky talisman and is a popular gem for gamblers.

Legends say that it is an all-purpose healer, used to reduce stress, develop confidence and imagination, and improve prosperity. An ancient legend from Tibet tells of its use to help nearsightedness and to improve the wearer's creativity.

Many crystal healers believe that Aventurine has the capacity to calm a troubled spirit, balance emotions and bring an inner peace. It is also believed to enhance leadership qualities allowing the wearer to act decisively, with strong intuitive power.

Just the facts

Aventurine is a Chalcedony that contains small inclusions of one of several shiny minerals which give the gem a glistening effect. The glistening effect of Aventurine is known as "aventurescence." The color of the aventurescence depends on the mineral included in the gem. Mica inclusions give the gem a yellow or silver glitter or sheen. Goethite and Hematite inclusions give the gem a red or gray glitter or sheen. Fuschite inclusions give the gem a green sheen.

Aventurine ranges in color from green, peach, brown, blue and creamy green. If a color is not stated with the word Aventurine, it is usually assumed to be green. In the past, Green Aventurine has been miscalled "Indian Jade."

BERYL

The name Beryl is from the ancient Greek "beryllos" for the precious blue-green color of sea water. This was originally applied to all green gemstones, but later used only for Beryl. Some scholars believe the word Beryl is related to the ancient trading city of Belur or perhaps has ancient Indian origins (being derived from the old Hindi word "velurya" or the Sanskrit word "vaidurya").

As an allochromatic gem, when absolutely pure Beryl is totally devoid of color. Small amounts of metallic elements can be present in the crystal structure, giving rise to many color variations. Aquamarine (page 21), Bixbite (page 26), Emerald (page 44), Fire Beryl™ - Goshenite (page 51) and Heliodor (page 63) are all members of the Beryl family.

Just the facts

Gemstone color varieties that belong to Beryl with specific names are listed below. All other colors of Beryl are simply referred to by their color (e.g., Yellow Beryl).

Aquamarine	Pastel greenish blue to blue
Bixbite	Red
Emerald	Green
Fire Beryl™ (Goshenite)	Colorless
Heliodor	Yellowish green
Morganite	Pastel pink to salmon apricots

Golden Beryl 14K Yellow Gold Ring

Beryl is famous for its perfect, six-sided prismatic hexagon crystals that usually occur individually. These are occasionally enormous and some 26-foot, well-crystallized examples are known to have existed. Understandably, only very small amounts of these enormous crystals are of a sufficient quality to be used in jewelry.

All Beryl varieties can be faceted into various gem cuts, and some Beryl displays phenomena including asterism (star effect), chatoyancy (cat's eye effect) and an unusual effect in Emerald called trapichism.

Golden Beryl

BERYL:	Perfect, prismatic hexagon crystals
Origins:	Afghanistan, Brazil, Colombia, Pakistan & South Africa
Colors Found:	Various
Family:	Beryl
Hardness:	7.50 - 8.00
Refractive Index:	1.56 - 1.61
Relative Density:	2.60 - 2.90

BIXBITE

Bixbite is the red variety of Beryl. Named after the mineral collector Maynard Bixby, Bixbite was discovered at the turn of the 20th century in the Thomas Range in Utah.

Bixbite is commonly called "Red Emerald" and occasionally referred to as "American Emerald."

Just the facts

Very scarce, Bixbite is only known to occur in a few areas of the western US, possibly one location in Mexico and possibly in Brazil. Bixbite suitable for faceting is extremely rare and is typically small in size (under 0.5 carats). The average size is 0.15 carats and the largest recorded Bixbite weighed 7 carats.

The "traditional" deposit for Bixbite, the Wah Wah Mountains, Utah has presently ceased operation. The last operators had to completely restore the site when they passed on their option. Apparently, anyone wishing to go back and re-open the mine will spend millions just removing overburden. There may still be lots of Bixbite in the ground at the location but its extraction hasn't proven to be economically viable.

Like Emeralds, inclusions in Bixbite are common, especially in specimens over 1 carat. However, its rarity and novelty for gemstone collectors has always been the primary factor.

BIXBITE:	Commonly known as Red Emerald
Origins:	US
Colors Found:	Red
Family:	Beryl
Hardness:	7.50 - 8.00
Refractive Index:	1.57 - 1.60
Relative Density:	2.66 - 2.70

CHALCEDONY

Chalcedony's (also spelled Calcedony, it is correctly pronounced as "Kal-ced-on-ee" and is the catchall term for cryptocrystalline Quartz) name is derived from Chalcedon or Calchedon, an ancient port of Bithynia, near present day Istanbul, Turkey. It has a waxy luster and appears in a great variety of colors including blue, white, buff, tan, green, red, gray, black, yellow or brown. Different colored varieties of Chalcedony have individual names including Agate (white, red, blue, gray, brown or black bands), Bloodstone (green with red spots), Chalcedony (blue to brownish blue), Chrysoprase (apple green), Carnelian (orange to red), Flint (dull gray to black), Jasper (spotted red, yellow, brown or green) and Sard (light to dark brown).

Legends and lore

The Romans prized Chalcedony as seals, and in the New Testament (Revelations 21:19) Chalcedony is one of the twelve gemstones set in the foundations of the city walls of Jerusalem. As compiled by Andreas, Bishop of Caesurae, one of the earliest writers to tie the Apostles with the symbolism of the twelve gems of Jerusalem, Chalcedony represented the Apostle St. Andrew.

Chalcedony was used during the Renaissance as a magic amulet to promote health and safety.

Chalcedony is one of the gemstones used in commesso or Florentine mosaic. Developed in Florence in the late 16th century, commesso is a technique of fashioning pictures with thin, cut-to-shape pieces of brightly colored gems.

*Chalcedony & White Topaz
14K Yellow Gold Men's Ring*

Chalcedony

Just the facts

Quartz gemstones are commonly separated into two groups based on the size of their individual crystals. The macrocrystalline Quartz (large crystal) group includes many popular gemstones such as Amethyst, Ametrine, Citrine and Green Amethyst (Prasiolite). Cryptocrystalline Quartz includes species whose individual crystals are too small to be easily distinguished. Apart from being a variety within the group, Chalcedony is also a catchall term to describe cryptocrystalline Quartz and includes many gems that have been coveted since antiquity.

Normally faceted as a cabochon it is often used to great effect in both necklaces and bracelets.

CHALCEDONY:	Waxy luster
Origins:	Brazil, India, Madagascar, Mexico, South Africa, Tanzania & US
Colors Found:	Black, blue, brown, buff, green, gray, red, tan, white & yellow
Family:	Quartz
Hardness:	6.50
Refractive Index:	1.54
Relative Density:	2.58 - 2.64

CHRYSOBERYL

The gem of springtime, youth and innocence, the name Chrysoberyl is derived from the Greek words for golden, "chryso," and green gemstone, "Beryl."

Its rarest variety, Alexandrite (the color change variety of Chrysoberyl), is quite well known, although the number of people who have heard of Alexandrite is probably 100 times greater than the number who have ever seen one, and 1,000 times greater than the number who have ever owned one.

Legends and lore

Said to bring peace of mind and increase self-confidence, Chrysoberyl also promotes kindness, generosity, benevolence, hope, optimism, renewal, new beginnings, compassion and forgiveness.

Just the facts

When cut, Chrysoberyl is an extremely brilliant gem, ideal for everyday wear and is rapidly gaining in popularity.

Displaying attractive golden lemons, limes, greens, oranges and chocolates, together with an extreme brilliance, Chrysoberyl is exceptionally tough, making it ideal for everyday wear. The color in yellow Chrysoberyl is due to iron trace elements.

Chrysoberyl & White Topaz 14K Yellow Gold Ring

Cat's Eye Chrysoberyl is a translucent gem ranging in color from a honey yellow or honey chocolate to yellowish green to apple green. It is known for its reflected light effect called chatoyancy (cat's eye). This is achieved by cutting gems that have small, parallel "silk" inclusions into cabochons. As the gem is rotated, it exhibits a distinct, silvery white line across its dome that seems to open and close like a cat's eye. It is so coveted that if you just mention cat's eye, it is assumed to be in reference to Cat's Eye Chrysoberyl.

Chrysoberyl & White Topaz 14K White Gold Ring

Exceptional quality Chrysoberyl has recently been unearthed in Magara, Tanzania, a region made famous by Tanzanite and Tsavorite.

CHRYSOBERYL:	Chatoyancy
Origins:	Brazil, India, Madagascar, Russia, Sri Lanka, Tanzania, Zambia & Zimbabwe
Colors Found:	Brown, yellow & yellowish-green
Family:	Chrysoberyl
Hardness:	8.00 - 8.50
Refractive Index:	1.74 - 1.75
Relative Density:	3.50 - 3.80

Cat's Eye Chrysoberyl and Chrysoberyl

Chalcedony's (also spelled Calcedony, it is correctly pronounced as "Kal-ced-on-ee" and is the catchall term for cryptocrystalline Quartz) name is derived from Chalcedon or Calchedon, an ancient port of Bithynia, near present day Istanbul, Turkey. It has a waxy luster and appears in a great variety of colors including blue, white, buff, tan, green, red, gray, black, yellow or brown. Different colored varieties of Chalcedony have individual names including Agate (white, red, blue, gray, brown or black bands), Bloodstone (green with red spots), Chalcedony (blue to brownish blue), Chrysoprase (apple green), Carnelian (orange to red), Flint (dull gray to black), Jasper (spotted red, yellow, brown or green) and Sard (light to dark brown).

CHRYSOBERYL

The gem of springtime, youth and innocence, the name Chrysoberyl is derived from the Greek words for golden, "chryso," and green gemstone, "Beryl."

Its rarest variety, Alexandrite (the color change variety of Chrysoberyl), is quite well known, although the number of people who have heard of Alexandrite is probably 100 times greater than the number who have ever seen one, and 1,000 times greater than the number who have ever owned one.

Legends and lore

Said to bring peace of mind and increase self-confidence, Chrysoberyl also promotes kindness, generosity, benevolence, hope, optimism, renewal, new beginnings, compassion and forgiveness.

Just the facts

When cut, Chrysoberyl is an extremely brilliant gem, ideal for everyday wear and is rapidly gaining in popularity.

Chrysoberyl & White Topaz 14K Yellow Gold Ring

Displaying attractive golden lemons, limes, greens, oranges and chocolates, together with an extreme brilliance, Chrysoberyl is exceptionally tough, making it ideal for everyday wear. The color in yellow Chrysoberyl is due to iron trace elements.

Cat's Eye Chrysoberyl is a translucent gem ranging in color from a honey yellow or honey chocolate to yellowish green to apple green. It is known for its reflected light effect called chatoyancy (cat's eye). This is achieved by cutting gems that have small, parallel "silk" inclusions into cabochons. As the gem is rotated, it exhibits a distinct, silvery white line across its dome that seems to open and close like a cat's eye. It is so coveted that if you just mention cat's eye, it is assumed to be in reference to Cat's Eye Chrysoberyl.

Chrysoberyl & White Topaz 14K White Gold Ring

Exceptional quality Chrysoberyl has recently been unearthed in Magara, Tanzania, a region made famous by Tanzanite and Tsavorite.

CHRYSOBERYL:	Chatoyancy
Origins:	Brazil, India, Madagascar, Russia, Sri Lanka, Tanzania, Zambia & Zimbabwe
Colors Found:	Brown, yellow & yellowish-green
Family:	Chrysoberyl
Hardness:	8.00 - 8.50
Refractive Index:	1.74 - 1.75
Relative Density:	3.50 - 3.80

Cat's Eye Chrysoberyl and Chrysoberyl

Also colloquially know as Cat's Eye or Australian Jade, its name comes from the Greek words "chrysos," meaning gold and "prason," meaning leek, due to its color similarities with the vegetable.

One of the most coveted varieties of Chalcedony Quartz, Chrysoprase is prized for its opalescent apple green color and rarity.

CHRYSOPRASE

Legends and lore

Chrysoprase was used by the Greeks, Romans and Egyptians in jewelry and other ornamental objects. In ancient Egyptian jewelry, Chrysoprase was often set together with Lapis Lazuli.

Chrysoprase is mentioned in the Bible as being one of the twelve gemstones set in the foundations of the city walls of Jerusalem (Revelations 21:19) and is the symbol of the Apostle St. Thaddeus.

Chrysoprase was very popular in the 14th century when the Holy Roman Emperor Charles IV used it to decorate chapels including the Chapel of Saint Wenceslas in Prague.

Chrysoprase was also a favorite gem of Frederick the Great of Prussia and Queen Anne of England.

Chrysoprase is believed by crystal healers to increase grace and inner equilibrium.

Chrysoprase 14K Yellow Gold Ring

Just the facts

Chrysoprase can vary in color from yellowish green to apple green and grass green depending on the levels of hydrated silicates and nickel oxides present in the gem.

Because of its semi-opaque green color, Chrysoprase was often mistaken for Imperial Jade (Jadeite).

Other types of green Chalcedony include Prase (a very rare less vivid green Chalcedony found in eastern Europe and in Delaware and Pennsylvania) and Mtorolite (a variety of green Chalcedony colored by chromium found in Zimbabwe).

Chrysoprase 14K White Gold Ring

Chrysoprase

CHRYSOPRASE:	Mentioned in the Bible
Origins:	Australia, Brazil, Madagascar, Russia, South Africa, Tanzania & US
Colors Found:	Apple green
Family:	Chalcedony Quartz
Hardness:	6.50
Refractive Index:	1.54
Relative Density:	2.58 - 2.64

CITRINE

Citrine is the yellow variety of macrocrystalline Quartz that takes its name from "citron," the French word for lemon. Citrine is a beautiful transparent gemstone and one of November's birthstones.

Legends and lore

Citrine was first used in jewelry in Greece during the Hellenistic period (end of the 4th to the end of the 1st century BC).

The first use of Citrine by the Romans was in intaglios (a gem carved in negative relief) and cabochons in the first centuries after the birth of Christ.

In antiquity, Citrine was believed to be the gemstone of happiness and used as a protective talisman against evil thoughts.

Among its many historic medicinal uses, Citrine was believed to aid digestion, remove toxins from the body (Citrine was once commonly used as a charm against snakebites and venomous reptiles), provide protection against the plague and bad skin, and to be useful in the treatment of depression, constipation and diabetes.

Among crystal healers, Citrine is said to be especially useful in stimulating one's mental capacities, enhancing creativity and intuition and bolstering one's self-confidence. It is also said to give emotional control while making one more alert. Citrine is also said to be very helpful in assisting one to acquire and maintain wealth.

Citrine 14K Yellow Gold Ring

Just the facts

Citrine occurs naturally in proximity to Amethyst and is a related Quartz mineral. The color of Citrine is due to small amounts (approximately 40 parts per million) of iron in the crystal structure of Quartz.

Citrine ranges in color from pastel lemon yellow to golden yellow to mandarin orange and "Madeira" red, after the color of the wine. Traditionally, the "Madeira" shades were more coveted, but these days many people prefer Citrine's brighter lemon tones. Most of the Citrine mined today comes from Uruguay, Brazil and many African nations including Madagascar. Citrine can be easily confused with Topaz and has even been called "Topaz Quartz."

Citrine

Multi Color Citrine beautifully melds the bright golden yellows of Citrine with the ice whites of White Quartz in one gem. Multi Color Citrine occurs

CITRINE:	November's birthstone
Origins:	Brazil, Madagascar, Mozambique, Tanzania, Uruguay & Zambia
Colors Found:	Shades of yellow
Family:	Quartz
Hardness:	7.00
Refractive Index:	1.50
Relative Density:	2.60 - 2.70

because of environmental changes during formation. At different times, the color-causing element (iron) was incorporated into the crystal, causing different color layers. Purposely cut to showcase this feature, Multi Color Citrine is generally judged by the balanced contrast between its colors. Cutting the gem so both colors show is sometimes challenging for cutters. While notoriously difficult to cut consistently, a well cut multicolored gem is a real delight.

CLINOHUMITE

Clinohumite (correctly pronounced "Klie-no-hue-might") is an extremely rare mineral that is occasionally faceted into bright attractive gemstones. Even though Clinohumite is a gemstone you hardly ever see, it has become increasingly popular, particularly among collectors. As all its deposits are scarce and only sporadically mined, Clinohumite remains one of the world's rarest gemstones with only a few thousand carats known to exist in private collections. A relatively new niche gem, Clinohumite has all the makings of a gem superstar: rarity, durability (similar to Tanzanite) and of course, beauty. Possessing visual similarities to Hessonite Garnet, rich vibrant crimson tangerine colors are always in demand by savvy jewelry connoisseurs.

Just the facts

A magnesium silicate, Clinohumite is an uncommon member of the Humite group of minerals. It was first discovered in metamorphosed limestone blocks that were ejected by the volcano Mount Vesuvius, near Napoles, Campania, Italy in 1876. Clinohumite is named after the mineral Humite in allusion to its monoclinic symmetry (a system of crystallization in which the crystals have three unequal axes) as opposed to Humite's orthorhombic symmetry (a system of crystallization characterized by three unequal axes intersecting at right angles). A very rare exotic gem, Clinohumite has only been available for about 20 years.

Clinohumite & Diamond 14K Yellow Gold Ring

Today, only 3 sources of gem quality Clinohumite exist: the Pamir Mountains of Tajikistan (discovered in 1983), the Taymyr region, northern Siberia, Russia (discovered in 2000) and Morogoro region, Tanzania (discovered in 2000). The current Tanzanian deposit in the Uluguru Mountains, Morogoro region was likely first discovered in 2004 or 2005.

Clinohumite

With a striking clarity, brilliance and luster, Clinohumite's colors are typically vivid crimson tangerines, although yellow, orange, red and browns also exist. Clinohumite is a fluorescent mineral and will glow a yellow-orange color when subjected to shortwave UV light.

Found in the marbles of contact metamorphic environments, Clinohumite is mined directly from host rock (calcite or limestone). Usually found as tiny indistinct grains, facet grade crystals are extremely difficult to find and are typically small (less than 1 carat).

CLINOHUMITE:	Extremely rare exotic gemstone
Origins:	Russia, Tajikistan & Tanzania
Colors Found:	Dark reddish brown, bright yellow to orange or brownish orange
Family:	Humite
Hardness:	6.00
Refractive Index:	1.63 – 1.67
Relative Density:	3.13 – 3.75

CORNELIAN (CARNELIAN)

Also known as Sadoine or Mecca Stone and sometimes spelled Carnelian, the name is derived from the Latin world for flesh, "carne," due to its orangey red color.

Legends and lore

Carnelian has been an important gem in nearly every great civilization. From the royalty of Ur (the Mesopotamian capital of pre-biblical times), to Napoleon (he returned from his Egyptian campaign with a huge octagonal Carnelian) and Tibetan Buddhists, Carnelian has been revered for its healing, spiritual and creative qualities.

A deeply religious gem, Carnelian was used by the Egyptian goddess Isis to protect the dead on their journey through the afterlife.

Carnelian is mentioned in the Bible as being one of the "stones of fire" (Ezekiel 28:13-16) given to Moses for the breastplate of Aaron (Exodus 28:15-30) and is also one of the twelve gemstones set in the foundations of the city walls of Jerusalem (Revelations 21:19). It is the symbol of the Apostle Philip.

Popular in ancient Greece and Rome for intaglio (a gem carved in negative relief) signet rings, the Romans symbolically associated dark colored Carnelian with men and light colored Carnelian with women.

Muhammad's seal was an engraved Carnelian set in a silver ring.

To this day, Buddhists in China, India and Tibet believe in the protective powers of Carnelian and often follow the Egyptian practice of setting the gem with Turquoise and Lapis Lazuli for enhanced power.

Just the facts

Carnelian is a translucent orange to red variety of Chalcedony. Uniformly colored cryptocrystalline Quartz, its red tints are caused by iron oxide trace elements.

CARNELIAN:	Mentioned in the Bible
Origins:	Brazil, India, Madagascar, Sri Lanka & Uruguay
Colors Found:	Orange to red
Family:	Chalcedony Quartz
Hardness:	7.00
Refractive Index:	2.65 - 2.66
Relative Density:	1.543 - 1.554

"I never worry about diets. The only carrots that interest me are the number of carats in a Diamond."

Mae West

DIASMOND

The word Diamond comes from the Greek word "adamas," meaning unconquerable or invincible.

"Diamonds are forever," sang Shirley Bassey, while Marilyn insisted they were "a girl's best friend." Celebrated in song, over the last century Diamond (April's birthstone) has become the most marketed of gemstones.

Legends and lore

The myths and facts associated with the Diamond transcend cultures and continents.

The world's first known reference to this gemstone comes from an Indian Sanskrit manuscript, the Arthsastra (which translates as The Lesson of Profit) written by Kautiliya, a minister to Chandragupta of the Mauryan Dynasty (322 BC – 185 BC).

Plato wrote about Diamonds as living beings, embodying celestial spirits.

Roman literature makes its first distinct mention of Diamonds only in the 1st century AD, in reference to the alluvial Diamonds found in India.

The ancient Greeks and Romans believed they were tears of the gods and splinters from falling stars. Cupid's arrows were supposed to be tipped with Diamonds, thus having a magic that nothing else can equal.

Diamond 14K White Gold Ring

The Hindus believed that Diamonds were created when bolts of lightning struck rocks. They even placed them in the eyes of some of their statues.

Jewish high priests turned to Diamonds to decide the innocence or guilt of the accused. A Diamond held before a guilty person was supposed to dull and darken, while a Diamond held before an innocent person glowed with increasing brilliance.

The Romans wore Diamonds because they were thought to possess broad magical powers over life's troubles, being able to give to the wearer strength, invincibility, bravery and courage during battle.

Kings of antiquity led the battles wearing heavy leather breastplates studded with Diamonds and other precious gems because it was believed that Diamonds possessed god-given magical qualities and powers far beyond the understanding of humankind. Thus, warriors stayed clear of kings and those who were fortunate enough to have the magical Diamonds in their breastplates.

A collection of Diamond White Gold Rings

DIAMOND

An act of Louis IX of France (1214-1270) established a sumptuary law reserving Diamonds for the King, indicating the rarity and value of this gem.

Until the 14th century only kings could wear Diamonds, because they stood for strength, courage and invincibility. Small numbers of Diamonds began appearing in the 14th century in European regalia and jewelry, set mainly as an accent among Pearls. But the possession of extraordinarily large and noble Diamonds was always the privilege of royal houses and rich families. As an example, the imperial crown of the Russian Tsarina Catherine the Second (1729-1796) was mounted with 4,936 sparkling Diamonds.

In the Middle Ages and the Renaissance, every ring set with a precious gem was not considered as much a piece of jewelry, but more as an amulet that bestowed magical powers upon its wearer. When set in gold and worn on the left side, it was believed that Diamonds held the power to drive away nightmares, to ward off devils and phantoms, and soothe savage beasts. A house or garden touched at each corner with a Diamond was supposed to be protected from lightning, storms and blight. Diamonds were also supposed to impart virtue, generosity and even to calm the mentally ill.

Not only was it commonly believed that Diamonds could bring luck and success, but also that they could counter the effects of astrological events.

Diamond 14K White Gold Ring

Just the facts

As a gemstone lover, you may have heard about the 4 C's related to valuing gemstones and in particular, Diamonds. While other factors such as origin sometimes need to be taken into consideration when valuing colored gemstones, below is a basic guide to the four C's that gemstone professionals and connoisseurs the world over rely on: cut, color, clarity and carat weight.

Color

Colorless and near-colorless Diamonds are rare, beautiful and highly prized among connoisseurs. To the untrained eye, most Diamonds look white. However, to the professional there are small differences in the degrees of whiteness seen.

A collection of Diamond White Gold Rings

DIAMOND

Cut

With round brilliant cut Diamonds accounting for over 80% of Diamond sales worldwide, ask anyone "What shape is a Diamond?" and they will probably say round. Despite this shape, there are many other beautiful Diamond cuts that warrant serious consideration. The eight most popular Diamond cuts are emerald cut, heart cut, marquise cut, oval cut, round brilliant cut, pear cut, princess cut and radiant cut.

Unlike colored gemstones, Diamonds are cut, shaped and proportioned to a remarkably uniform ideal. In 1919, the Russian mathematical genius Marcel Tolkowsky, a member of a large and powerful Diamond family, published his opinions of what Diamond proportions result in the optimum balance of brilliance and fire.

Carat weight

As mentioned above, unlike gemstones, Diamonds are cut to a uniform ideal for maximum brilliance (white light reflections), fire (flashes of color) and scintillation (patterns of light and darkness). With this uniform cutting and proportions, we can very conveniently and accurately equate Diamond carat size with their millimeter size.

Diamond 14K White Gold Ring

Round Brilliant Cut Diamond	
1 millimeter	0.01 carat
2 millimeter	0.03 carat
3 millimeter	0.10 carat
4 millimeter	0.25 carat
5 millimeter	0.50 carat
6 millimeter	0.75 carat
6.5 millimeter	1.00 carat
7 millimeter	1.25 carat
7.5 millimeter	1.65 carat

Clarity

Inclusions are tiny natural irregularities within the body of a Diamond. Nearly all gemstones contain some inclusions, however many are microscopic and can only be seen under magnification. While the prevalence and acceptability of inclusions varies from

Diamond 14K Yellow Gold Ring

DIAMOND

Yellow Diamond 14K Yellow Gold Ring

Blue Diamond

Yellow Diamond

gemstone to gemstone, in general, if they do not interfere with the beauty of a gemstone, they are not only accepted, but are also a fascinating hallmark of authenticity that records a gem's natural relationship with the earth.

What is the GIA Diamond Grading System?

Developed by the GIA (Gemological Institute of America), this system is now commonplace for the retailing of Diamonds across the globe and consists of a Diamond Clarity Scale and a Diamond Color Scale.

GIA Diamond Clarity Scale

(FL) FLAWLESS: Shows no inclusions or blemishes of any sort under 10X magnification when observed by an experienced grader.

(IF) INTERNALLY FLAWLESS: Has no inclusions when examined by an experienced grader using 10X magnification, but will have some minor surface blemishes.

(VVS1 and VVS2) VERY VERY SLIGHTLY INCLUDED: Contains minute inclusions that are difficult even for experienced graders to see under 10X magnification.

(VS1 and VS2) VERY SLIGHTLY INCLUDED: Contains minute inclusions such as small crystals, clouds or feathers when observed with effort under 10X magnification.

(SI1, SI2 and SI3) SLIGHTLY INCLUDED: Contains inclusions (clouds, included crystals, knots, cavities and feathers) that are noticeable to an experienced grader under 10X magnification. The SI3 Diamond clarity grade was created because many in the Diamond industry felt that there was too wide a gap between SI2 and SI1. After the EGL (European Gemological Laboratory) started issuing certificates with the SI3 grade, the Rapaport Diamond Report (the definitive price guide for Diamonds) added SI3 to its price list.

(I1, I2 and I3) INCLUDED: Contains inclusions (possibly large feathers or large included crystals) that are obvious under 10X magnification.

(PK) PIQUE: Inclusions easily visible to the naked eye.

GIA Diamond Color Scale

Prior to the introduction of the GIA grading system, the letters A, B and C were used to grade Diamonds.

DIAMOND

As the GIA wanted a fresh start, they decided to begin with the letter D.

D, E, F. These purest tints are rare and comparatively expensive. Their rare color assigns them a higher market price.

G, H, I. Often offering much better value, to the untrained eye they seem the exact same color as the more expensive D, E and F colors.

J, K, L. Discounted for their barely perceptible yellowish tints, Diamonds in this range offer excellent value.

M - Z. Further discounted for their more distinct yellow hues. Diamonds outside the normal color range are called "fancy colors" and come in about any color you can imagine (e.g., pink, red, green, purple, black, blue, yellow and more).

Pairs and Suites

Pairs or suites of Diamonds matched for color, clarity and cut are more highly valued per carat or per gem than single Diamonds of the same quality. Given the rarity of many Diamonds, a matching set is disproportionately hard to find and thus commands a higher per carat price than if each of the Diamonds from the suite were sold separately.

Black & White Diamond 14K Yellow Gold Ring

Colored Diamonds

Most Colored Diamonds found in jewelry today are normally treated. The process known as color enhancement involves using clean Diamonds and modifying their color with a combination of electron bombardment and heat using safe electron-accelerator technology. This enhancement exactly duplicates the "natural process" Colored Diamonds undergo during their formation within the earth. All color enhanced Diamonds sold by GemsIV are treated in the US to certified international standards.

Unlike some other Diamond treatments, Color Enhanced Diamonds are treated to fulfill preferences for vivid color only; this coloring technique does not try to hide or dissipate flaws. The myriad of popular Diamond colors produced using this technology includes blue, green, red, orange, yellow, pink, purple and black. The real beauty and popularity of these Diamonds lies in the fact that they combine both the rich color hues of colored gems such as Rubies and Sapphires, with the unforgettable

Red Diamond

DIAMOND:	April' s birthstone
Origins:	Africa
Colors Found:	Various
Family:	Carbon
Hardness:	10.00
Refractive Index:	2.41
Relative Density:	3.50

DIAMOND

brilliance and sparkle of a Diamond. In other words, they virtually become "two gems in one."

What are Conflict Diamonds?

A Conflict Diamond (also called a Blood Diamond) is a Diamond mined in a war zone and sold, usually clandestinely, in order to finance an insurgent or invading army's war efforts. The Kimberley Process is a global system to eradicate Conflict Diamonds and has two parts:

1. A government-regulated system adopted in 2000 by more than 40 countries, the United Nations, and the Diamond industry to control the export and import of rough Diamonds across borders. It requires that rough Diamonds mined after January 1, 2003 be shipped in tamper-resistant containers and accompanied by government-validated Kimberley Process Certificates. Only participating countries may legitimately export rough Diamonds and only to co-participating countries.

2. To strengthen the government program, the international Diamond and jewelry industry represented by the World Diamond Council (WDC) initiated and committed to a voluntary system of warranties. It requires that every time Diamonds (rough, polished or Diamond jewelry) change hands, the seller will affirm on the invoice that the Diamonds have been purchased through authorized channels not involved in funding conflict.

Naturally, GemsTV is Kimberley Process compliant.

Diopside was named in 1800 from the Greek word "dis" meaning double and "opsis" meaning vision, in reference to the pleochroism (different colors displayed when viewed from different angles) found in its prismatic form.

DIOPSIDE

Legends and lore

Diopside is also called the "crying gemstone," because it is believed by crystal healers to heal trauma by bringing forth cleansing tears.

Diopside is assumed to bring creativity to the wearer and is said to be related to love and commitment. Crystal healers believe that, when worn close to the chest (such as in a pendant), Diopside can benefit the heart, lungs and circulation.

Just the facts

Diopside is a calcium magnesium silicate found in metamorphosed impure limestone, meteorites and igneous basalts. Diopside has been previously named Schefferite, White Schefferite and Zinc-Schefferite.

Diopside is the magnesium-rich member of the "monoclinic-pyroxene series" that occurs when ions (and magnesium) freely substitute each other.

Russian Diopside 14K White Gold Ring

Diopside crystals have a perfect cleavage in two directions, are often twinned and are short and columnar, but with an uneven fracture. Mineralogists easily recognize Diopside in the field by its crystals, its color, its fracture, its cleavage and its white or white-green streak.

Diopside is typically white, blue, purple, brown, green, colorless and gray with a glassy luster. The less common shades are yellowish brown and greenish brown.

Varieties of Diopside include "Russian Diopside" (a chromium-rich Diopside known for its deep green color), "Violan" (a rare blue variety found in Italy), "Cat's Eye Diopside" (green with the effect due to inclusions of rutile needles), "Malacolite" (a white colored variety), "Salaite" (an iron variety), "Dekalbite" (an iron-free variety) and "Star Diopside" (a star with four rays).

Gem quality Diopside is mined in Siberia, Italy, Sri Lanka, Brazil, Madagascar, South Africa and Pakistan. Uzbekistan, located between Tajikistan and Turkmenistan, is becoming an important locality for a variety of Russian Diopside called Tashmarine. This

*Russian Diopside & White Topaz
14K Yellow Gold Ring*

DIOPSIDE

Russian Diopside & White Topaz
14K Yellow Gold Ring

Russian Diopside

DIOPSIDE:	Perfect cleavage in two directions
Origins:	India & Russia
Colors Found:	Blue, brown, colorless, green, gray, purple & white
Family:	Pyroxene
Hardness:	5.00 - 6.00
Refractive Index:	1.66 - 1.72
Relative Density:	3.20 - 3.60

variety has a slightly lower chromium content than the Siberian material, a less saturated color and can display gray or brown tones. India has the largest deposits of Cat's Eye or Star Diopside. The color of African Diopside tends to be a more yellowish color similar to Peridot.

Russian Diopside

Russian Diopside has a beautiful rich green color, similar to that of the best Emeralds or the rarest Tsavorite Garnets.

Colored by chromium, Russian Diopside is also known as Chrome Diopside and Imperial Diopside. While there is little historical information regarding this rare gem type, some claim it is beneficial for health, relationships, spirituality and financial success. Many people within the industry feel that Russian Diopside should be a birthstone for May.

One major reason Russian Diopside is relatively unknown is that it has only recently become available in sizable commercial quantities. Interestingly, a company recently trademarked the name "Vertelite" for Russian Diopside. The name was created from "verte," the Latin word for green and "lite," the Latin word for tone.

Russian Diopside displays strong birefringence and has a vitreous luster. It is mostly available in small sizes, with large carat weights hard to find.

Russian Diopside is mostly mined in Yakutia, Siberia. Yakutia territory is located in the extreme north of Asia and is considered the coldest place in the northern hemisphere. Mining is limited due to cold winters lasting for nine months; hence this gem is seasonal and it has been difficult to maintain a steady supply.

Interestingly, Yakutia is also the source of 99% of all Russian Diamonds. Russian Diopside is a Diamond mine indicator mineral and is sometimes found as an inclusion inside Diamonds. The liberalization of the economy of the former Soviet Union has made Russian Diopside more available than ever before.

Star Diopside

Star Diopside is also known as "Black Star Diopside" because of its blackish color. Asterism, or the star effect, is a reflection that appears as two or more intersecting bands of light across the surface of a gem.

Star Diopside has four rays, two of which are straight, while the other two are not at right angles to the first pair.

Star Diopside is mainly mined in India and is generally a black or blackish green color.

Cat's Eye Diopside

A green variety of Diopside, chatoyancy or the cat's eye effect is a reflection that appears as a single bright band of light across the surface of a gemstone. Cat's Eye Diopside is mainly mined in India.

Violan

Violan is light blue to purple in color due to the presence of large amounts of manganese. Violan is mined mainly in Italy.

EMERALD

For more than 4,000 years, the deep "green fire" of Emeralds has been treasured as a symbol of eternal spring and immortality.

Shrouded in myth and lore, the birthstone for May isn't just a beautiful gem: Emeralds are also ornaments of power and politics that have created legends and molded world history.

Prized by Egyptians, Romans, Aztecs, crowned heads of Europe, and today, gem connoisseurs the world over, Emeralds, more than any other precious gemstone have sparked the eternal fires of our collective imagination.

Legends and lore

Spring is a time of growth and rejuvenation. Nothing reflects this more than the intense green shades of an Emerald, May's birthstone.

Emeralds are regarded by many cultures as a symbol of personal development. It was once thought that Emeralds possessed the power to soothe the soul and sharpen wit.

Majestic Emerald & Diamond 18K Yellow Gold Ring

Some people believe that wearing an Emerald brings wisdom, growth and patience. And as any couple would agree, all of these qualities are essential for lasting love. This may explain why a gift of Emerald is considered symbolic of love and devotion. Emeralds are even believed to change color upon infidelity!

Emeralds have long been thought to possess healing powers. While today we know that Emeralds are not a cure for all medical and psychological problems, many people still use Emeralds to soothe their eyes and bring them good health. In fact, green has long been considered a soothing color and it is no coincidence that the "green room" in theaters and TV studios is supposed to relax a performer after the stress and eyestrain of studio and stage lights.

Majestic Emerald & Diamond 18K Yellow Gold Ring

A truly ancient gemstone, there is archaeological evidence that the Babylonians may have been marketing Emeralds as early as 4000 BC.

The history of Egyptian Emeralds dates back over 4,000 years. Located in Egypt's eastern desert region, ancient miners braved extreme heat, scorpions and snakes to search for the "green fire." Interestingly, Greek miners once labored in the Egyptian desert for Alexander the Great.

The ancient mines of Egypt were rediscovered in 1818 by the French explorer Caillaud. Finding the mine

EMERALD

with the help of the Egyptian government, he noted that Emeralds were probably mined there long after the kings and queens of Egypt ruled the land.

The Egyptians were known to engrave Emeralds with the symbol for foliage to represent eternal youth, burying these jewels with their dead.

Emeralds were said to be the favorite gem of Cleopatra. She often wore lavish Emerald jewelry and bestowed visiting dignitaries with large Emeralds carved with her likeness when they departed Egypt.

Egyptian Emeralds were first mined some 2,000 years before Cleopatra's birth. During her reign, Cleopatra claimed these Emerald mines as her own, as well as the world's oldest source of Peridot, the fog-wrapped desert isle of Zeberget (St. John's Island). Zeberget Peridot has a uniquely Emerald-like color, due to its high nickel content. This is probably why many of Cleopatra's "Emeralds" were later found to be Peridot.

The ancient Romans associated Emerald with fertility and rebirth, dedicating it to Venus, their goddess of love and beauty. The Roman historian Pliny the Elder once said of Emeralds, "nothing green is greener," and recorded that the Roman Emperor Nero, while presiding over gladiatorial fights, wore spectacles made of Emeralds. However, gemologists now believe that this was highly unlikely as the ancient Egyptian Emerald produced crystals of insufficient size and clarity needed for such an instrument. Historians now believe that Fire Beryl™ was probably the gem used.

Majestic Emerald & Diamond 18K Yellow Gold Ring

The legends and lore surrounding Emeralds would not be complete without recounting the infamous stories of the Conquistadors, Hernando Cortés, who started his campaign against the Aztecs in 1519, and Francisco Pizarro, who commenced his military operation against the Incas in 1526. When Hernando Cortés planted the Spanish flag on Aztec soil, he snatched from the defeated Emperor Moctezuma an enormous pyramid shaped Emerald so big it could be seen from 299 feet away!

Majestic Emerald 18K White Gold Ring

Just the facts

The neon green color of Emeralds is unparalleled in the gem kingdom. Its beautiful green color, combined with its rarity, makes Emerald one of the world's most valuable gemstones. Interestingly, its name comes from the Greek word "smaragdos," meaning green gem.

Emerald & Diamond 14K Yellow Gold Pendant

EMERALD

Majestic Emerald & Diamond 18K Yellow Gold Ring

*Siberian Emerald & Diamond
14K Yellow Gold Pendant*

Emeralds are a member of the Beryl family of minerals. Minute traces of chromium, vanadium and iron give Emeralds their famous "green fire." The green crystals grow slowly within metamorphic rocks and are restricted in size by the host rock, making large Emeralds rare and costly.

Unlike other Beryl, Emeralds often contain inclusions and tiny fractures. These are commonly called "jardin," from the French word for "garden," because of their resemblance to foliage. For Emeralds, jardin is not looked on as a negative aspect as it would be for some other gem varieties, but instead is considered part of Emerald's character and can be used to assure the purchaser of a natural gemstone.

Although Emerald is relatively hard and durable, it must be protected from harsh blows because the jardin found within make it susceptible to breaking. The famous "emerald cut" was developed specifically for this gem to reduce the amount of pressure exerted during cutting.

Transparent Emeralds are faceted in gem cuts for jewelry, while translucent material is cut and polished into cabochons and beads. Trapiche Emeralds are also cut into cabochons, making exquisite jewelry pieces.

A very small number of Emeralds display asterism and chatoyancy; these too are cut into cabochons.

When buying Emeralds the most important consideration is always color, with clarity and quality of cut playing second fiddle. Nevertheless, the brightness of the gemstone (which is somewhat determined by the cutting and clarity) is also an important factor.

Traditionally, deep green is the most desired color in Emeralds. Paler Emeralds are sometimes called "Green Beryl."

While we have generally not broken down the different features of gems from different locations, we felt that the Emerald was worthy of geographical analysis.

Colombian Emerald

Known for their vivid green color, Colombian Emeralds are usually of exceptional quality. Colombia is by tradition and lore, the finest modern source for Emeralds.

"Indeed there is no stone, the color of which is more delightful to the eye; for whereas the sight fixes itself with avidity upon the green grass and the foliage of the trees, we have all the more pleasure in looking upon the Emerald, there being no green in existence of a more intense color than this."

Pliny the Elder

EMERALD

With each comprised of many individual mines, there are three main areas of Emerald mining in Colombia: Muzo, Coscuez and Chivor.

Muzo Colombian Emerald

The famed Muzo mines lay 100 miles north of Bogota. Emerald crystals from Muzo tend to have more saturated color than either Coscuez or Chivor. They are considered some of the finest Emerald mines in the world.

A rare, prized form of Emerald, found only in the Muzo mining district of Colombia, Trapiche Emeralds are extremely unusual. Star-shaped rays that emanate from its center in a hexagonal pattern characterize these Emeralds. These rays appear much like asterism, but unlike asterism, they are not caused by light reflection from tiny parallel inclusions, but by black carbon impurities that happen to form in the same pattern.

Coscuez Colombian Emerald

The Emerald crystals of Coscuez tend to exhibit a very wide range of colors but unfortunately also tend to be more included than those from Muzo. While Muzo and Coscuez are Colombia's most prolific Emerald producing locales, with the majority of Colombian Emeralds seen on the world market coming from these two areas, today Coscuez produces approximately sixty percent of Colombia's "green fire."

Chivor Colombian Emerald

Chivor Emeralds are best known for their bluish cast and generally have fewer inclusions and a lighter color than either Coscuez or Muzo Emeralds. The Chivor mining area is the smallest of the three and is separate from Muzo and Coscuez, which lay adjacent to each other.

Brazilian Emerald

While Colombian Emeralds are known for their vivid green color, Brazilian Emeralds are known for their variety of color, ranging from light green to medium dark blue green.

Emeralds were first discovered in Brazil about 500 years ago after the arrival of the Portuguese. However,

Siberian Emerald & Diamond 14K White Gold Ring

Siberian Emerald & Diamond 14K Yellow Gold Ring

it was only in 1963 when the first samples with commercial value were found in Bahia, close to the town of Paraiso du Norte in northern Brazil, effectively wiping out the notion that Brazil had no real "green fire" of its own.

Pakistani Emerald

While an extremely harsh climate prevents the mining of Emerald deposits at higher altitudes, at lower elevations in the Swat Valley of Pakistan lay the Gujar Kili Mine, and the ancient and historically significant Mingora Mine. Gallo-Roman earrings featuring Mingora Emeralds have been discovered. Severe weather conditions restrict operations during winter, making the hand-dug output very limited. The Pakistani government tightly controls the mining of Emeralds from relatively new deposits discovered in 1960 in the Himalayan Mountains.

Siberian Emerald

Siberian Emerald is long prized for its breathtaking crystal clarity, green fire and forest green hues.

According to history, Siberian Emerald was discovered by a Russian peasant, Maxim Stefanovitch Koshevnikov, in 1830 in the roots of a tree that had been felled in a storm on the Tokovoya River near Ekaterinburg in Siberia's Ural Mountains. Despite this, rumors persist that Russia actually supplied Emeralds long before the Spaniards discovered the famous Colombian Emerald in the late 16th century. These legends even go as far as to suggest that the Scythian Emeralds mentioned by Pliny the Elder in his "Historia Naturalis" came from the Urals.

Rising to fame in the 19th century, the largest and best known source of Siberian Emerald is the Mariinsky (St. Mary's) Mine. This mine was discovered in 1833 near the village of Malyshevo. The deposits were nationalized after World War I and Emerald mining soon ceased when Malyshevo became a military security zone. Siberian Emeralds almost entirely disappeared; thankfully, Siberian Emerald is now back and we are delighted to offer an amazing selection to GemsTV customers! Siberian Emerald is mined in very rugged terrain - the area is wet, rocky and very mountainous, and less than half a percent of the rough crystals mined are suitable for faceting. As a result, Siberian Emeralds are a "must have" for any true Emerald connoisseur.

EMERALD

Siberian Emerald & Diamond 14K Yellow Gold Ring

Emerald

EMERALD:	May's birthstone
Origins:	Brazil, Colombia, Pakistan, Siberia, Zambia & Zimbabwe
Colors Found:	Green
Family:	Beryl
Hardness:	7.00 - 8.00
Refractive Index:	1.57 - 1.58
Relative Density:	2.67 -2.78

EMERALD

Zambian Emerald

Zambian Emeralds are of very high quality. Although Zambia has the world's second largest Emerald deposit, it is substantially underdeveloped and primarily restricted to artisanal mines near Kagem, Kitwe, Miku and Mufulira in remote northern Zambia. As basic hand tools are mainly used to mine Zambian Emerald, this limits supply, increasing its rarity and value. Zambian Emerald is extracted from talc-magnetite schists Zambian miners call "paidas" (when it's unaltered) and "chikundula" (when it's weathered). They call small Emerald crystals that may be indicative of bigger crystals "ubulunga."

The Majestic Emeralds offered on GemsTV are from Zambia. At GemsTV, "Majestic" is our own term used to describe superior quality (color and clarity) in gemstones and in our opinion, Majestic Emerald is some of the best Emerald available.

While most members of the Beryl family (commonly known as the "mother of gemstones") such as Emerald or Aquamarine are famous for their colors, Fire Beryl™ is the highly collectible clear variety that displays a Diamond-like fiery brilliance.

FIRE BERYL™ (GOSHENITE)

Legends and lore

The traditional gemological name for this gemstone is Goshenite but at GemsTV we prefer our exclusive name Fire Beryl™. So named for its distinctive fiery brilliance, high luster and colorless purity, it's easy to see why Fire Beryl™ has long been compared with Diamonds. Naturally, at GemsTV our expert gem graders use years of skill and expertise to ensure that only the finest examples worthy of the name Fire Beryl™ are selected.

The name Goshenite is derived from the location of its first discovery, Goshen, Massachusetts. Fire Beryl™ is also known as White Beryl or Lucid Beryl.

Fire Beryl™ is an enduringly popular gemstone and has been used in jewelry since antiquity. The ancient Greeks even used Fire Beryl™ as lenses in the first spectacles!

Fire Beryl™ 14K Yellow Gold Ring

Just the facts

Interestingly, pure Beryl is colorless, with traces of different metallic elements being responsible for this gem family's great color range. Since Beryl's color varieties are caused by metallic elements and pure Beryl is colorless, one could assume that Fire Beryl™ is Beryl in its purest form. However, this is not technically correct as some metallic elements in natural Fire Beryl™ actually inhibit the colors that result from other metallic elements that may also be present.

Fire Beryl™ & White Zircon 14K Yellow Gold Ring

Fire Beryl™

FIRE BERYL:	Also known as White or Lucid Beryl
Origins:	Afghanistan, Brazil, Colombia, Pakistan & South Africa
Colors Found:	Colorless
Family:	Beryl
Hardness:	7.50 – 8.00
Refractive Index:	1.57 – 1.60
Relative Density:	2.60 – 2.80

51

FLUORITE

Deriving its name from the Latin word "fluere," meaning to flow (in reference to its low melting point), Fluorite is known as "the world's most colorful gemstone."

Fluorite, from which we get the word fluorescent, crosses the entire color spectrum, from deep purple to crimson red, blue to green (Chrome Fluorite) and frosty orange to lemon yellow. Fluorite is one of the more famous fluorescent minerals. Many specimens strongly fluoresce, in a great variety of colors.

Legends and lore

According to crystal healers, Fluorite is a Third Eye gem bringing rationality to intuitive qualities. It is believed to offer a stabilizing energy, facilitating order, balance and healing. Fluorite is also believed to be excellent for fostering clarity of mind, objectivity, concentration and meditation.

Just the facts

Due to its glassy luster Fluorite is highly coveted. Fluorite is the natural crystalline form of calcium fluoride and often forms beautiful cube-shaped crystals. It is a transparent to translucent glassy mineral. When pure, Fluorite is colorless; however, it usually contains impurities that color it. The most common colors are violet, blue, green, yellow, brown, pink and bluish black.

Fluorite & White Topaz 14K Yellow Gold Ring

Arguably, the most popular color for Fluorite is a deep purple that can rival Amethyst in its finest examples. Indeed Fluorite/Amethyst comparisons are often used to show that color cannot be relied upon as a gemstone test.

An eye catching phenomenon of Fluorite is its distinctive bicolor and multicolor banding. Chunky Fluorite bead strands optimize this exceptional effect. Interestingly, the "blue john" variety mined in England that possesses curved bands of blue purple, violet, yellow and white has been used as an ornamental gem since Roman times.

Fluorite

Color Change Fluorite is mined in Bihar, India and shows a dramatic change from green to purple. Color change gems are those that distinctly change their color when viewed under two different light sources.

FLUORITE:	Comes in many colors
Origins:	Brazil & India
Colors Found:	Various
Family:	Fluorite
Hardness:	4.00
Refractive Index:	1.43
Relative Density:	3.20

GARNET

Garnet has a history spanning more than 5,000 years. Deriving its name from the Latin word for seed, "granatus," Garnet was so named because of its similar color to pomegranate seeds.

From the svelte necklines of Abyssinian princesses to the powdered décolletage of Marie Antoinette, the captivating mystique of Garnets has made them a timeless symbol of feminine beauty. The imaginative lure of this "queen of gems" intoxicates the senses.

Understanding the Garnet Family

Garnets are a group of minerals all having essentially the same crystal structure but varying in chemical composition, physical properties and colors. Unlike many other gemstones, color in Garnet does not come from chemical impurities - when pure, a Garnet still has color. Garnets very rarely occur in nature with their compositions precisely matching their "pure ideal." A natural Garnet's composition typically falls somewhere in between the pure ideals of other Garnet members.

*Mandarin Garnet & White Topaz
14K Yellow Gold Ring*

Group	Species	Pure Types	Mixed Types
Pyralspites	Almandine	Almandine	Rhodolite (Pyrope & Almandine)
	Pyrope	Pyrope	Mozambique (Pyrope & Almandine)
	Spessartite	Spessartite (Mandarin & Tangerine)	Malaia (Intermediate composition range between Spessartite & Pyrope)
			Umbalite (Pyrope & Almandine with small traces of Spessartite)
Ugrandites	Andradite	Demantoid	Mali (Andradite & Grossular)
	Grossular	Grossular, Tsavorite, Merelani Mint & Hessonite	
	Uvarovite		

*Mozambique Garnet & White Topaz
14K Yellow Gold Ring*

GARNET

Color Change Garnet in different lighting conditions

Legends and lore

Garnet's associated symbolism with pomegranates has been longstanding. Interestingly, several ancient pieces of jewelry have been unearthed that are studded with tiny red Garnets in cluster-like patterns reminiscent of pomegranates. The pomegranate is associated with eternity in Greek mythology and mentioned specifically in the legend of Hades' abduction of Persephone.

Garnet has long been associated with fire and was thought to possess the ability to illuminate the sky at night. Today, Garnets remain a symbol of faith, truth and light. This story from Grimm's fairytales nicely presents this association – "Once upon a time an elderly lady came upon an injured bird. Taking the bird home with her, she nursed it back to health until one day it flew away. Although the lady thought she'd never see it again, it returned to her house with a Garnet that she put by her bedside. To her surprise, she awoke every night to see it shining as bright as a torch, illuminating the bird's gratitude for her kindness."

According to Jewish legends, during the great flood a radiant Garnet guided the way for Noah, ultimately leading his ark to salvation. For Muslims they are believed to illuminate the fourth heaven.

Garnet jewelry was buried with Norsemen to light their passage to Valhalla and was also used to light the palace of Abyssinia's monarch.

The Crusaders set Garnets into their armor, believing their power would lead them to safety. During the Middle Ages Garnet was also believed to draw out negativity, ward off harm and increase well-being, chivalry, loyalty and honesty.

To receive a Garnet as a gift in the Middle Ages was considered good luck, however, if ever stolen, bad luck to the thief! It was also believed that a Garnet's loss of luster was a sign of impending doom.

Although Garnet was the "fashion gem" of the 18th and 19th centuries, the inadequacy of available chemical tests often resulted in it being confused with dark Ruby. Jewelry set with Garnets from Czechoslovakia was particularly admired, and although today the Garnets are mined elsewhere, Bohemian style Garnet jewelry has retained its popularity.

In 1912 Garnets were made the official birthstone for January by the American National Association of

Jewelers. It is also the gemstone for Aquarians and a traditional gift for 2nd and 6th wedding anniversaries.

Just the facts

Even though there are many types of Garnets (including trade and historic names there are currently 38 known Garnet names), appearing in as many colors, when you say "Garnet" most people automatically think of small dark red gemstones. In fact, Garnets offer enough variety for every taste and can consequently keep up with the fast pace of changes in fashion!

Champagne Garnet

A distinctive and very attractive color variety of Malaia Garnet, Champagne Garnet is in fact a mixture of Pyrope and Spessartite Garnet and is mined in Tanzania's Umba Valley.

Color Change Garnet

Color Change Garnets are one of the rarest, most interesting and phenomenal of all gemstones. An extremely rare variety of Malaia Garnet, Color Change Garnet is in fact a mixture of Pyrope and Spessartite Garnet. Comparatively, it is slightly rarer than Alexandrite and it is a constant struggle to get enough quantity to craft lines of jewelry. As our selection is usually relatively limited, it is one of those gems that discerning customers should purchase when they see it, as it simply isn't always available.

Mandarin Garnet & Diamond 14K Yellow Gold Ring

While Color Change Garnets have been reported since the early 1970's, it was only noted as a curiosity by a very small number of gemologists and gem collectors because of very limited quantities and colors that were viewed more as strange rather than beautiful. This situation dramatically changed in 1987 when Russian Alexandrite-like Color Change Garnets were discovered in Tanzania's Umba Valley. Since this time, Color Change Garnets have become increasingly coveted by gem collectors and jewelry connoisseurs alike. Historically, color change gems have been popular since the discovery of Alexandrite in the 19th century.

The Madagascan varieties generally display greens (including bluish greens) when viewed under sunlight, changing to raspberries (reddish purples) under candlelight. The Tanzanian varieties generally

Mali Garnet & White Topaz 14K Yellow Gold Ring

GARNET

Mali Garnet & White Topaz 14K Yellow Gold Ring

*Color Change Garnet & White Topaz
14K White Gold Ring*

Demantoid Garnet

display khaki olive limes when viewed under sunlight, changing to orange crimson reds under candlelight. However, other color varieties of Color Change Garnet exist - in daylight their color ranges from shades of green, beige, brown, gray and blue (in hues more synonymous with Blue Spinel rather than Sapphire), but in incandescent light they appear a reddish or purplish/pink color. The color change can be intense and equal to the color change of top quality Alexandrite. As a result, Color Change Garnets can easily be mistaken for Alexandrite.

Discovered in the late 1990's, Madagascan Color Change Garnet is from Bekily in southern Madagascar, while Tanzanian Color Change Garnet is today predominately sourced from Tunduru in Tanzania's Ruvuma region. It is also found in some parts of the United States, Russia, Turkey and Sri Lanka (in very small quantities).

Color Change Garnets are not usually found in large sizes. According to one source, the largest known faceted Color Change Garnet weighed 9.5 carats. The most dramatic color changes in Color Change Garnets are due to high amounts of vanadium (in contrast to chromium which causes color change in Alexandrite), although chromium is responsible for the color change in some Color Change Garnets. The existence of additional coloring agents, such as manganese, can also cause some of the more delicate colors in this Garnet variety.

Demantoid Garnet

Demantoid Garnet is one of the most desirable of all colored gemstones and extremely rare. Discovered in 1855 in the Russian central Ural Mountains at two alluvial deposits, it was first assumed to be Emerald, and even took the name "Uralian Emerald" until gemologists took a closer look.

The name Demantoid originates from the old German word "demant" meaning "Diamond-like," because of a luster and dispersion that yields a fire even higher than Diamonds!

Commonly known as "horsetail" inclusions, some Demantoid Garnets have golden byssolite strands that form beautiful patterns similar to the tail of a horse. Demantoid Garnets with prominent horsetail inclusions are particularly coveted.

While small scale mining reportedly recommenced in Russia in 1991, most Demantoid Garnets are sourced

GARNET

from relatively new deposits beneath the scorched desert sands of Namibia. A favorite of the famous Russian goldsmith Karl Fabergé, due to a fire greater than that of Diamonds, Demantoid Garnet is an absolute "must have" for any serious collector.

Hessonite Garnet

A variety of Grossular Garnet, Hessonite comes in two colors, golden and cinnamon (this variety is commonly known as the "Cinnamon Stone"). A perfectly colored Hessonite is a bright golden orange that resembles a combination of honey and orange with an internal fire. Some Hessonites have tints of red and brown.

Popular for thousands of years, the ancient Greeks and Romans used it in jewelry, cameos and intaglio (a figure cut into a gem so as to make the design depressed below the surface, whereas in a cameo the relief rises above the surface). Interestingly, its name comes from the Greek word "esson," meaning inferior, because it is slightly softer than other Garnet varieties. However, please don't be put off by the origin of its name. Hessonite is still durable and perfectly suited to jewelry.

Hessonite Garnet 14K Yellow Gold Ring

Widely used in Vedic astrology, Hessonite is known as "Gomedha" in Hindi. The ancient Hindus believed that Hessonite was formed from the fingernails of the great demon Vala, which were scattered in the lakes of the East. Vedic astrologers believe that when set in gold, Hessonite is a powerful talisman that increases your lifespan and happiness.

Hessonite is common in the gem gravels of Sri Lanka and practically all Hessonite is obtained from this locality, although it is also found in Africa.

Mozambique Garnet & White Topaz 14K Yellow Gold Ring

While the clearest gems are most prized, inclusions in Hessonite are common, with unique toffee-like streaks giving Hessonite an oily or even glasslike appearance.

Malaia Garnet

Discovered in the mid 1960's in Tanzania's Umba Valley, this red-orange to pink-orange variety of Garnet was originally thought to be Spessartite Garnet.

Actually a mixture of Pyrope, Almandine and Spessartite, Malaia Garnets are lively gems that exhibit sparkling red flashes. Once discovered not to be

GARNET

Mali Garnet & White Topaz 14K Yellow Gold Ring

Tangerine Garnet 14K Yellow Gold Pendant

Spessartite, it aptly became known by the Swahili word "Malaia" meaning "outcast."

Malaia Garnets are available in numerous shades of orange, ranging from soft peach to intense reddish orange.

Mali Garnet

Mali Garnet is one of the latest discoveries in the Garnet family. Mali Garnet is an attractive and very interesting rare mixture of Andradite and Grossular that was only discovered in late 1994 at the Sandaré Mine in Mali's Kayes region (Diakon Arrondissement). Extremely rare, Mali Garnets are a bright, uniform light yellowish green color.

Mandarin, Tangerine & Spessartite Garnet

Mandarin and Tangerine Garnets are the intensely bright color varieties of the rare orange red Spessartite Garnet, also known as Spessartine.

Spessartite Garnet is named after its first discovery in Spessart, Bavaria in the mid 1800's. Spessartite Garnet, once an extremely rare gem, is now enjoying a newfound popularity.

In 1991 Mandarin Garnets were discovered embedded in mica in northwest Namibia where the Kunene River borders Namibia and Angola. In 1994 new deposits were unearthed in southwest Nigeria. Soon after, Tanzania, the powerhouse of African gems, yielded deposits at the fabled gemstone mines of Arusha and Lelatema.

Although initially called "Kunene Spessartine" or "Hollandine," the evocative names Mandarin Garnet and Tangerine Garnet were soon adopted.

Merelani Mint Garnet

Long regarded as a source of the finest colored gems, it is no surprise that Tanzania is home to some of the world's most coveted Garnets. Displaying stunning mint greens, luster, sparkly brilliance and excellent durability, Merelani Mint Garnet is a relatively new rare gemstone whose popularity is only limited by its scarcity.

Named for its color and where it is mined, Merelani Mint Garnet was first discovered around 1998 in the same area as Tanzanite (Merelani Hills, Arusha region, Tanzania). Merelani Mint Garnet is basically a different

GARNET

hue of its better known relative, Tsavorite Garnet (Grossular Garnet). Extremely scarce, Merelani Mint Garnet is always relatively small in size (under 1 carat) and is usually included with bubbles and/or silk. Not surprisingly, when clean, Merelani Mint Garnet increases in value.

Formed in metasomatic conditions (the process by which the chemical composition of a rock is changed by interaction with fluids), it is typically extracted directly from metamorphic rocks and similar to Tanzanite, it is found in association with graphite.

Stunning green Garnets have historically always been in very high demand and Merelani Mint Garnet is coveted for a very good reason - few Garnets have such a brilliant appeal.

Mozambique Garnet

Originating in the east African nation they are named after, Mozambique Garnets are famed for their high quality and wonderfully warm, red colors.

Mozambique Garnet is a mixture of Pyrope and Almandine Garnet, similar in color to Rhodolite Garnet, but slightly redder and darker.

Pyrope Garnet

Hear the word "Garnet," and what invariably comes to mind is the image of the deep red Pyrope Garnets belonging to the pyralspites family. Pyrope comes from the Greek word "pyropos," meaning "fiery eyed."

Fine Pyrope Garnets may be visually confused with dark rubies. It was the "fashion gem" of the 18th and 19th centuries and many Rubies of this period were later found to be Pyrope Garnets.

Rhodolite Garnet

The name "Rhodolite" is taken from the Greek "rho'don" and "lithos," which literally translate to "rose stone." Possessing a color reminiscent of the rhododendron flower, this name was first used in the late 19th century to describe Garnets discovered in North Carolina.

Unusually striking, Rhodolite is a naturally occurring blend of Almandine and Pyrope Garnet. While raspberry is the most prized color, Rhodolite is also found in shades of pink through lavender.

Rhodolite Garnet & White Topaz
14K Yellow Gold Ring

Rhodolite Garnet & White Topaz
14K Yellow Gold Ring

GARNET

Tsavorite Garnet 14K Yellow Gold Ring

Tsavorite Garnet & White Topaz 14K Yellow Gold Ring

*Tangerine Garnet & White Topaz
14K Yellow Gold Ring*

Rhodolite is typically found as water worn pebbles in alluvial deposits but it is also occasionally mined directly from host metamorphic rock. The most spectacular Rhodolite is mined in Sri Lanka, Zimbabwe, and from a relatively new deposit in the Kangala area of Tanzania that was discovered in 1987. Since then, gorgeous raspberry hued Rhodolite has been found in other regions of Tanzania including Ruvuma, Mtwara and Lindi.

Tough, durable, never enhanced and easily cleaned, Rhodolite is ideal for jewelry. Due to its bright transparent clarity, Rhodolite is often cut into fantasy shapes.

Star Garnet

A highly unusual form of Garnet is the rare four-rayed Almandine Star Garnet. While Almandine Garnets (also known as "Almandite") are the most common variety of Garnets, those displaying the star are not at all common. Available in deep reds, Almandine Star Garnets are found in Nigeria and Tanzania.

Asterism or the star effect is a reflection effect that appears as two or more intersecting bands of light crossing the surface of a gem.

Tsavorite Garnet

For some the sixties swung, for gemologists they rocked. The decade which had most people looking to the sky for Lucy's Diamonds had gemologists transfixed by a myriad of precious gemstones hailing from Africa's arid savannas: Fancy Sapphires, Rubies, Tourmaline, Tanzanite, a plethora of gorgeous colored Garnets, among them a brilliant green Grossular Garnet, Tsavorite. Tsavorite, East Africa's beautiful green gemstone is rightful heir to the title "the King of Garnets."

Some 40 years after its discovery, Tsavorite has comfortably established itself as one of the world's most beautiful, precious and desirable gemstones. Tsavorite Garnet, comparable in scarcity to Demantoid Garnet, is extremely rare. In fact, it is so rare that it might be unavailable in future years.

First discovered in 1967 by the now legendary Scottish geologist, Campbell R. Bridges, Tsavorite has quickly found favor as a precious colored gem of choice. Bridges first discovered Tsavorite in Tanzania, but in those days getting an export license to take the gems out was impossible. Bridges, aided by the local Masai and Kikuyu tribesmen persisted in his search, but this time turned his attention to the neighboring country of Kenya. In 1971 Bridges discovered Tsavorite for a second time in Kenya's Tsavo region.

Life in Africa's bush is dangerous and the Tsavo region is well known as the domain of man-eating lions and poachers. In order to protect himself from predators and brigands, Bridges was forced to live in a tree house. And as he didn't want his treasure to be stolen, he cunningly used the locals' fear of snakes by placing a python in among the Tsavorite rough.

Tsavorite eventually found its way to America where Henry Platt of Tiffany & Co. named the gemstone, basing its name on the famous Tsavo National Park in Kenya. Tsavorite took the world by storm and interest increased dramatically when in 1974 Tiffany's started a special campaign promoting Tsavorite, making it well known in the US. International promotional campaigns followed and soon global demand for Tsavorite reached epic proportions.

While Tsavorite was once being mined in 40 different areas throughout Tanzania and Kenya, only four mining ventures are still producing commercial quantities. While some 50 deposits have been found in Kenya, Tanzania, Madagascar and even Zambia, only a handful of small mines are viable. This is because Tsavorite is notoriously difficult to mine, requiring a good understanding of geology. Seams suddenly disappear, giving no indication where to look next and its crystals are often found inside Quartz or Scapolite "potatoes" that must be cracked open to reveal the Tsavorite.

Tsavorite's intense green colors, similar to the very best Emeralds, are due to the presence of vanadium in the host rock. Like all Garnets, Tsavorite possesses few inclusions and its high index of refraction results in a superb brilliance. While by no means an absolute, Kenyan Tsavorite generally possesses deeper color saturation than those from Tanzania.

Umbalite Garnet

Umbalite Garnet is an attractive light pinkish-purple Garnet that was first unearthed in Tanzania's Umba Valley in 1978. A cocktail of Pyrope, Almandine, with small traces of Spessartite Garnet, production of this unusual gem material has been irregular and it is highly sought after by connoisseurs of fine gemstones.

GARNET

GARNET:	January's birthstone
Origins:	Kenya, Madagascar, Mali, Mozambique, Namibia, Nigeria, Russia, Sri Lanka & Tanzania
Colors Found:	Various
Family:	Garnet
Hardness:	6.5 - 7.5
Refractive Index:	1.70 - 1.73
Relative Density:	3.51 - 3.65

GREEN AMETHYST (PRASIOLITE)

Green Amethyst can be a confusing gem as it is traded under a variety of names and is even sometimes mistaken for other gemstones such as Peridot and Tourmaline. The green variety of Quartz, Green Amethyst is also known as Vermarine, Green Quartz, and Lime Citrine or by its gemological name, Prasiolite. Although reasonably affordable, it is unusual and remains a collector's gemstone.

Mostly mined in Brazil, Green Amethyst's gemological name is derived from the Greek words "prason," meaning leek (due to its color similarities with the vegetable) and "lithos," meaning stone.

Legends and lore

Green Amethyst is believed by crystal healers to facilitate the gap between the physical and spiritual aspects of life, attracting prosperity through strengthening the mind, emotions and will.

Just the facts

Although Quartz of sufficient beauty to be set into jewelry is not available in great abundance, Quartz is found in many geological environments and is a component of almost every rock type. It is also the most varied in terms of varieties, colors and forms. Quartz gemstones are often separated into two groups based on the size of their individual crystals. Green Amethyst is a macrocrystalline Quartz (large crystal) and this group includes many popular gemstones such as Amethyst, Citrine and Ametrine. All forms of Quartz are piezoelectric (when heated or rubbed they create an electrical charge becoming a magnet that attracts lightweight objects), making for important applications in electronics. Tourmaline is the only other gemstone that possesses this property.

Green Amethyst & White Topaz 14K Yellow Gold Ring

With beautiful colors ranging from pastel to deep forest green, Green Amethyst is a tough gemstone, making it ideal for everyday wear.

*Green Amethyst & White Topaz
14K Yellow Gold Pendant*

GREEN AMETHYST:	Green variety of Quartz
Origins:	Brazil
Colors Found:	Shades of green
Family:	Quartz
Hardness:	7.00
Refractive Index:	1.54 – 1.55
Relative Density:	2.65

Green Amethyst

Heliodor was first discovered in Rossing, Erongo in western Namibia in 1910 and was named from the Greek "helios" and "doron," meaning "gift from the sun."

Displaying characteristic yellowish greens (similar to olive oil), Heliodor is a variety of Beryl, the "mother of gemstones." Interestingly, as an allochromatic gem, pure Beryl is colorless, with traces of different elements being responsible for Beryl's great color range.

Legends and lore

Among crystal healers, Heliodor has traditionally been used as a charm to promote compassion, sincerity and sympathy. Heliodor is also believed by some to enhance one's intuition and to improve one's communicative abilities.

Just the facts

Heliodor's main characteristic is its color, which is produced when iron replaces some of the aluminum in the crystal structure. The color ranges depending on the relative concentrations and location of iron within the Beryl crystal structure. However, the shade may vary and it is often difficult to establish a dividing line between Heliodor, Golden Beryl and Yellow Beryl. Originally, Golden Beryl found in Namibia was called Heliodor, but today the name is used to describe the yellowish green varieties of Beryl, with the golden colors called Golden Beryl and the yellow colors called Yellow Beryl. However, please be aware that these demarcations are still confused by some sources.

Not surprisingly, Heliodor was discovered in a pegmatite that also produced Aquamarine, a Beryl also colored by iron. Like Aquamarine, the more intense colors frequently have more inclusions. Heliodor occurs primarily in granite pegmatites and to a lesser extent in granite cavities. Because of Heliodor's relatively robust hardness and specific gravity, it is sometimes found in alluvial deposits.

Heliodor is famous for its perfect, six-sided prismatic hexagonal crystals that usually occur individually. These are often enormous and some 26-foot, well crystallized examples are known to have existed. Understandably, only very small amounts of these enormous crystals are of a sufficient quality to be used in jewelry.

Heliodor, Ice Zircon™ & White Topaz 14K Yellow Gold Ring

Heliodor

HELIODOR:	Perfect, prismatic hexagon crystals
Origins:	Brazil, Madagascar, Namibia, Nigeria & Russia
Colors Found:	Yellowish-green
Family:	Beryl
Hardness:	7.50 - 8.00
Refractive Index:	1.57 - 1.60
Relative Density:	2.80

HELIODOR

Heliodor can be faceted into various gem cuts, and some gems display chatoyancy (cat's eye effect) when cut and polished into cabochons. When perfectly transparent, six-sided crystals are discovered, they are sometimes set uncut in necklaces and pendants.

While the best Heliodor traditionally hails from Namibia, beautiful specimens are also found in Minas Gerais, Brazil and the Ural Mountains, Russia. While Heliodor's durability and summery colors makes it well suited to jewelry, it is extremely difficult to find enough Heliodor to craft lines of jewelry, particularly with respect to clean examples displaying intense colors and a high luster (good cutting and polishing). It frequently simply isn't available and despite its beauty, rarely makes an appearance in jewelry.

HIDDENITE

Hiddenite is an attractive and rare gemstone. It has an unusual green color that is unlike either Peridot or Emerald. Hiddenite was discovered in 1800 in Hiddenite, a city in Alexander County, North Carolina. Both the city and the gem mineral were named after William Earl Hidden, a mineralogist and mining director from Newark, New Jersey who was mining in the area.

Just the facts

Hiddenite is actually one of the two varieties of Spodumene. The other is Kunzite, typically a pink to lilac variety, but Yellow Kunzite is a trade name used to describe yellow Spodumene. While all varieties of Spodumene are scarce, Hiddenite is the rarer of the two, with Kunzite better known by most gemstone collectors. Spodumene's color is due to trace elements of iron (producing yellow to green), chromium (producing medium to deep green) or manganese (producing pink to lilac), all substituting aluminum in the crystal structure. The name Spodumene (named by B.J. D'Andrada Sylva in 1800) was derived from the Greek "Spodumenos," meaning "burnt to ashes" in reference to some Spodumenes' light gray color.

The green color of Hiddenite ranges from a yellowish to a bluish green. Hiddenite is strongly pleochroic meaning that it can change color when viewed from different angles, thus a gem cutter must take great care to orient the gem in a position that accentuates its deepest color. The top and bottom of the crystal reveal the deepest colors and knowledgeable gem cutters take advantage of this effect to produce the finest quality Hiddenite.

Hiddenite 18K White Gold Ring

Hiddenite is formed from lithium aluminum silicate. The crystals are vitreous and can be either transparent or translucent. For many years, the occurrence of Hiddenite was limited to North Carolina, however new deposits were recently discovered in Madagascar and Brazil.

Typing "Hiddenite" into an internet search engine will provide hundreds of results about the city of Hiddenite in North Carolina. As you start to discover the lifestyle of this historic city, you can't help but become attached to this wonderful gem.

Hiddenite

HIDDENITE:	Pleochroism
Origins:	Brazil, Madagascar & US
Colors Found:	Yellowish to a bluish green
Family:	Spodumene
Hardness:	6.50
Refractive Index:	1.65 - 1.68
Relative Density:	1.66

IOLITE

Iolite & White Topaz 14K Yellow Gold Ring

Iolite

IOLITE:	Also known as Water Sapphire
Origins:	India, Madagascar & Sri Lanka
Colors Found:	Violet blue, light blue or yellow gray
Family:	Cordierite
Hardness:	7.00 - 7.50
Refractive Index:	1.50
Relative Density:	2.53 - 2.65

The name Iolite comes from the Greek word "ios," which means violet. Iolite is a transparent, violet blue, light blue or yellow gray gemstone. A pleochroic gem (different colors are displayed when the gemstone is viewed from different angles), Iolite will show many colors in a single piece.

Legends and lore

According to ancient Scandinavian sagas, Norse navigators used thin pieces of Iolite (their magical "sun stone") as the world's first polarizing filter. Looking through an Iolite lens, they could determine the position of the sun on overcast days and navigate their boats safely. Hence Iolite is also known as the "Viking's compass" or "Viking's stone." The story of the "Viking compass" triggered the curiosity of a 10 year-old boy who just happened to be the son of the Chief Navigator of the Scandinavian Airline System, Jorgen Jensen. The "sun stone" described in Norse lore sounded similar to the twilight compass used by his father at higher latitudes where a magnetic compass is unreliable. His father's twilight compass was equipped with a polarizing filter that enables a navigator to locate the sun, even when it is behind the clouds, by light polarized by the atmosphere.

Intrigued by his son's observation, Jensen passed it onto Danish archaeologist Thorkild Ramskau, who immediately recognized its scientific implications. Collecting minerals found in Scandinavia whose molecules are aligned similarly to the crystals in a polarizing filter, Ramskau put Iolite (the gem variety of the mineral Cordierite) to the test. Accompanying navigator Jorgen Jensen on a flight to Greenland, Ramskau kept track of the sun with a piece of Iolite while Jensen used the twilight compass. Incredibly, his observations were accurate to within 2.5 degrees of the sun's true position!

Known as the gemstone of clear vision, when worn as an amulet, Iolite was believed to have the power to guide lost sailors to the brilliance of the sun, allowing them to safely find their way home.

Just the facts

Iolite is a popular and interesting gemstone. It has a pretty violet blue color that is unlike other gemstones although it has been compared to light blue Sapphires. It is for this reason that it is sometimes known as "water sapphire."

While we believe an Iolite necklace or Iolite earrings are probably the best ways to showcase this gem's unique color, Iolite rings are also desirable, as it is a durable gem well suited to everyday wear.

Pleochroism (different colors displayed when viewed from different angles) is very pronounced in Iolite and is seen as three different color shades in the same gem. In viewing an Iolite, the colors violet blue, yellow gray and a light blue can be seen. When correctly faceted, Iolite will show its best violet blue color through the top or table of the gem, but when viewed from another angle the gem may display other colors.

JADE (NEPHRITE)

For centuries, Nephrite Jade and the other Jade variety Jadeite were considered one and the same. It was not until 1863 in France that they were identified as different minerals with a similar appearance and properties.

The name Jade was first used around the time of the Spanish conquest of Central and South America and is from the Spanish "piedra de ijada," meaning hip stone, as it was thought to cure kidney stones and other kidney ailments.

While Jade was known as the "stone of heaven" in ancient China, the Chinese word for Jade, Yu, is not generally used. Jade was excavated from the Kunlun Mountains of northwest China, from 5000 BC, and even today China remains an important source for this gemstone.

Legends and lore

In Russia, it has been mined and crafted since 3000 BC. Tsar Alexander III's sarcophagus was carved from Jade. For about 3,000 years Jade has been highly prized by the Native Americans of British Columbia, Canada who called it "greenstone" and for centuries the New Zealand Maori have made beautiful Nephrite carvings.

Just the facts

Nephrite is composed of silica and magnesia and its color is determined by the amount of iron present in the mineral. A lesser iron content produces lighter colors such as white, cream, yellow, gray, green, blue, red, brown and lavender. A greater iron content produces the darker colored Nephrite, such as darker gray and darker green.

Nephrite has the highest tensile strength (toughness as opposed to hardness) of all natural gemstones and in fact has a tensile strength greater than some steel. It is so strong that it cannot be chiseled. It must be ground using sharp abrasives.

Interestingly, less than 0.05% of Nephrite extracted is of gem quality. Nephrite is typically not treated as it is less likely to take up dye or stains than Jadeite. Older pieces benefit from polishing to retain their luster.

Jade & Diamond 18K Yellow Gold Ring

JADE:	One of the toughest gems
Origins:	China
Colors Found:	Blue, brown, cream, green, gray, lavender, red, white & yellow
Family:	Jade
Hardness:	6.50
Refractive Index:	1.61 - 1.63
Relative Density:	2.90 - 3.10

JASPER

The name comes from the Latin name for Jasper "iaspis," which probably also referred to the other types of Chalcedony Quartz. Jasper is an opaque and fine grained variety of Chalcedony Quartz. It is typically found in red, yellow, brown or green colors and generally has spots.

Jasper is normally cut as cabochons and has traditionally been used as a gemstone for jewelry such as brooches, earrings, necklaces, pendants, intaglios (a gem carved in negative relief) and cameos (a gem carved in relief).

Legends and lore

Jasper was a favorite amulet gem in ancient times and is referenced in Greek, Hebrew, Assyrian and Latin literature. For example, Jasper is one of "the stones of fire" (Ezekiel 28:13-16) that were given to Moses at the mountain of God and said to possess the power to summon angels. Moses then decreed them mounted into a sacred breastplate for his brother, the high priest Aaron (Exodus 28:15-30). In the New Testament (Revelations 21:19), Jasper is one of the twelve gemstones set in the foundations of the city walls of Jerusalem. As compiled by Andreas, Bishop of Caesurae, one of the earliest writers to tie the Apostles with the symbolism of the twelve gems of Jerusalem, Jasper was denoted for the Apostle St. Peter.

In some Native American cultures, Jasper is considered to be the symbolic blood of the earth, and was thus thought to be one of the best gems for connecting with the deep, stabilizing energies of the earth.

Jade, Red Jasper & Mother of Pearl 925 Silver Watch

According to crystal healers, Jasper is an intensely protective gem, acting to stabilize the aura and rid it of dysfunctional energy thereby facilitating relaxation, contentment and compassion.

Just the facts

Quartz gemstones are commonly separated into two groups based on the size of their individual crystals. The macrocrystalline Quartz (large crystal) group includes many popular gemstones such as Amethyst, Ametrine and Citrine. Cryptocrystalline Quartz includes species whose individual crystals are too small to be easily distinguished. Apart from being a variety within the group, Chalcedony is also a catchall term to describe cryptocrystalline Quartz and includes Jasper as well as many other gems that have been coveted since antiquity.

Jasper

JASPER:	Mentioned in the Bible
Origins:	India, Madagascar & Mexico
Colors Found:	Brown, green, grayish white, pink, red, shades of bluish purple & yellow
Family:	Chalcedony Quartz
Hardness:	6.50 - 7.00
Refractive Index:	1.54
Relative Density:	2.59 - 2.61

KORNERUPINE

Kornerupine (also known as Prismatine) was discovered in Fiskernaes, Greenland in 1884 and was named after the Danish geologist and explorer Andreas N. Kornerup (1857-1881). It is a rare gemstone well known for its pleochroism (different colors seen from different viewing angles) and its green color, which can be as intense as Emerald.

Legends and lore

Among crystal healers, Kornerupine is considered a gemstone for teaching and communication. Kornerupine is also said to help stabilize the emotional swings of manic-depressives and assist in seeing through the false agreements in one's current reality.

Just the facts

A metamorphic mineral, Kornerupine is a complex magnesium aluminum borosilicate whose crystals are often found in alluvial deposits collected behind rocks or in the bends of rivers. Kornerupine is often deposited with other gems including Sapphire, Chrysoberyl, Ruby, Topaz, Garnet, Zircon, Diopside, Andalusite, Spinel and Iolite.

Kornerupine 14K Yellow Gold Pendant

While Kornerupine has a similar, but slightly higher index of refraction than Emeralds, as well as their characteristic inclusions, the two gems are easily distinguished by Kornerupine's pleochroism. Depending on the angle from which Kornerupine is viewed, its colors can range from brown, colorless, green, greenish-yellow, yellow, pink or lavender. However, wherever possible Kornerupine is faceted on the green axis as this coloration is its rarest and most coveted color.

Kornerupine

Kornerupine also occasionally exhibits chatoyancy or the cat's eye effect. When polished as cabochons Kornerupine can display a reflection effect that appears as a single bright band of light across its surface. This effect is caused by inclusions of fine, slender parallel fibers in the gem.

While Kornerupine is a rare gem that used to be limited to collections, it is now becoming increasingly popular in jewelry due to its suitability for everyday wear.

KORNERUPINE:	Pleochroism
Origins:	Madagascar, Sri Lanka, Tanzania
Colors Found:	Brown, green & orange
Family:	Kornerupine
Hardness:	6.50 - 7.00
Refractive Index:	1.66 - 1.68
Relative Density:	3.28 - 3.35

Kunzite, discovered in California in 1902, was named after Tiffany's chief gemologist, George Frederick Kunz.

Kunz described this durable pastel pink gemstone as having two distinct properties: "phosphorescence" where Kunzite, in this aspect similar to Diamonds, is observed to glow in a darkened room after it has been exposed to the sun's ultraviolet rays and "pleochroism," showing different colors when viewed from different directions.

These phenomena are best seen in larger sized gems set into jewelry like pendants, drop and chandelier earrings, and rings with open prong or bar settings that let light flow freely through them, accentuating Kunzite's fire to full effect.

Kunzite radiates pure Parisian chic, revealing delicate raspberry pinks, frosty lilacs, cool lavenders and hot fuchsias under the warm glow of incandescent light (candlelight). Its subtle coloring perfectly compliments "décolleté" eveningwear and soft candlelight, hence its colloquial name "the evening gemstone."

Legends and lore

Aside from their obvious physical beauty, pink gemstones possess potent metaphysical properties. Alternative healers use a multitude of pink gems in conjunction with the "heart chakra." The 4th of 7 energy points that run the course of the human body, the heart chakra is believed to carry the emotional sensibilities of love and compassion.

Some believe that when the 4th chakra is blocked we experience emotions such as anxiety, fear, anger and frustration. Crystal healers use the properties of pink gems like Pink Tourmaline and Kunzite to free the heart chakra from this negative energy.

This alternative approach of enhancing the "power of pink" is a viewpoint shared and supported by traditional methods of medicine and psychology:

"The color Pink causes the brain to send signals that reduce the secretion of adrenalin, reducing the heart rate and consequently dissipating states of extreme excitement such as anger." Science Digest, 1980

Just the facts

The lithium in Kunzite's chemical composition, lithium aluminum silicate, along with trace amounts

KUNZITE

Kunzite & Diamond 14K Yellow Gold Ring

Kunzite

KUNZITE:	Pleochroism
Origins:	Afghanistan, Brazil, Madagascar & Pakistan
Colors Found:	Shades of pink & yellow
Family:	Spodumene
Hardness:	6.00 - 7.00
Refractive Index:	1.65 - 1.68
Relative Density:	3.16 - 3.20

KUNZITE

of manganese, gives it a wonderful pink violet color that complements both autumn and spring wardrobes. As a member of the Spodumene family, Kunzite is closely related to Hiddenite, the green variety of Spodumene. Hiddenite is an attractive gem, but is extremely rare and for the most part is known only by collectors (see page 65). Spodumene's color is due to trace elements of iron (producing yellow to green), chromium (producing medium to deep green) or manganese (producing pink to lilac), all substituting for aluminum in the crystal structure.

While Kunzite is usually thought of as a pink to violet gemstone, Yellow Kunzite is a trade name used to describe Yellow Spodumene. Displaying delicate pastel lemon meringues, Yellow Kunzite hails from Madagascar and Afghanistan and possesses all the attributes of Kunzite, albeit in another color, providing Kunzite lovers with a delightful alternative.

Kunzite is strongly pleochroic, meaning there is a color intensity variation when a crystal is viewed from different directions. The top and the bottom of the crystal reveal the deepest colors. Our experienced gem cutters always take this into consideration when faceting Kunzite for GemsTV.

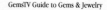

Also called Disthene, the name Kyanite is derived from the Greek "kyanos," meaning blue. The most popular varieties display intensely beautiful colors reminiscent of top Ceylon and Kashmir Sapphires. Although the name Kyanite has been used since 1789, Kyanite was sold in Europe as Sapphire until the turn of the 20th century.

Legends and lore

The powerful blue hues of Kyanite have long been thought to inspire calmness, composure, serenity, loyalty and respect.

Kyanite is used by alternative healers as a tool for meditation and relaxation. These healers use Kyanite to open the Third Eye chakra to enhance creativity, broaden perception and to reach a better understanding of others. Kyanite is also said to foster tranquility and believed to have a positive effect on dreams, visualization and foresightedness.

Just the facts

Like Diamonds, Kyanite has perfect cleavage in one direction, a unique characteristic among gemstones. This combined with its varying hardness (Kyanite is a rare polymorph, displaying two hardnesses within one gem), makes Kyanite a challenging gem to facet. Understandably, the cutting of Kyanite is an extremely important quality consideration.

Occurring in a wide variety of locations around the world, the best quality Kyanite hails from a deposit discovered in 1995 in the Kali Gandaki region of west central Nepal and Tibet. Tibetan Kyanite is arguably the best ever found, displaying rich cobalt blues, evocative of superb Sapphires.

Kyanite & White Topaz 14K White Gold Ring

Kyanite

KYANITE:	Perfect cleavage, varying hardness
Origins:	Nepal & Tibet
Colors Found:	Blue
Family:	Kyanite
Hardness:	4.50-7.00
Refractive Index:	1.71-1.73
Relative Density:	3.56-3.68

LABRADORITE

Labradorite is named after the Labrador Peninsula in Canada where it was discovered. Displaying brilliant pastels and deep golden colors, it even includes varieties colloquially known as "black rainbow," which feature a spellbinding play of color. Labradorite is a stunning gemstone perfect for wardrobes in all seasons.

Legends and lore

Calling it "firestone" because of its captivating play of color, the Native Americans of Labrador attributed mystical qualities to Labradorite, using the powdered gem as a magical potion to cure their ailments.

Interestingly, some modern mystics believe that Labradorite is a gem that assists the practice of magic, unleashes the power of the imagination and helps to overcome personal limitations.

Just the facts

Labradorite is a sodium-rich variety of plagioclase Feldspar. While transparent Labradorite is relatively free from inclusions and appears red, orange, yellow or colorless, the smoke gray varieties that show a rainbow-like color effect or "iridescence" are most frequently used in jewelry.

Valued for its lustrous metallic reflections (called schiller) that are said to resemble a butterfly's wing, this iridescence is aptly called "labradorescence" by gemologists and appears as stunning rainbow colored reflections when light strikes the gem in a particular direction. Mainly caused by the interference of light from lattice distortions, cracks or structural layers breaking up light into spectral colors, this effect often appears in violet, blue, green, yellow, gold and even reddish orange tints. Spectrolite, an extremely rare variety previously only found in Finland, but now also mined in India, can even display the complete color spectrum.

When appreciating the play of color in Labradorite, observe the strength and intensity of the labradorescence when the gemstone is viewed from different angles. This may result in different colors being visible or even a range of colors all visible at the same time.

LABRADORITE:	Labradorescence
Origins:	China, India & Madagascar
Colors Found:	Colorless, orange, red, smoke gray & yellow
Family:	Feldspar
Hardness:	6.00-6.50
Refractive Index:	1.55-1.57
Relative Density:	2.70-2.72

The word "lapis" is the Latin word for stone. The names of both "lazuli" and Lazurite are derived from the Persian word "lazhuward" and Latin word "lazulum" that means blue or heaven. The Lapis Lazuli name, often shortened to Lapis, is sometimes mistakenly used for the mineral Lazurite.

Legend and lore

Lapis was mentioned in writing in 2650 BC in the Sumerian epic of Gilgamesh and in the book of Exodus in the Bible. The ancient Egyptians used Lapis extensively in religious ceremonies (it appears in various passages in the Egyptian Book of the Dead), and Lapis items were found in royal tombs, including that of Tutankhamen. The ancient city of Ur had a thriving trade in Lapis as early as the fourth millennium BC.

The Greeks and Romans used it as a reward for bravery and the Romans also believed Lapis to be a powerful aphrodisiac. The Greeks and Romans also employed it for inlaid work and for jewelry, amulets and talismans. They named it "sapphirus" (blue), which is now used for the blue variety of Corundum, Sapphire.

When Lapis was first introduced to Europe, it was called Ultramarinum, meaning beyond the sea. Lapis was once powdered and mixed with oil to produce the pigment ultramarine, which is seen in the beautiful blues of Renaissance paintings. Ultramarine has been made synthetically since 1828.

Lapis Lazuli 925 Silver Men's Ring

In the Middle Ages, it was thought to keep the limbs healthy and free the soul from error, envy and fear. In the 17th century, it was used in medicine to prevent miscarriages, epilepsy and dementia.

Attributed with great healing, purifying and curative properties, Lapis allegedly points the way to enlightenment, and aids in the opening of the Third Eye. Popular with ancient alchemists, it was used in medicine, cosmetics and paintings. It was also believed to confer ability, success, divine favor, ancient wisdom and cure sore throats. No wonder it was once as valuable as gold!

The Arab geographer Istakhri recorded a visit to the Afghanistan Lapis mines in the 10th century and Marco Polo visited and wrote about them in 1271.

Lapis Lazuli

LAPIS LAZULI:	Early jewelry gem
Origins:	Afghanistan & Pakistan
Colors Found:	Ultramarine
Family:	Lazurite
Hardness:	5.00 – 6.00
Refractive Index:	1.50
Relative Density:	2.50 – 3.00

LAPIS LAZULI

Just the facts

Mined in the Kochka river valley of Badakhshan, Afghanistan for over 7,000 years, the "Armenian stone" is an enduring rock - and yes, it is a rock! Lapis is a contact metamorphosed limestone that contains Lazurite, Pyrite and Calcite. Unlike other gems, it is a composite of several materials with sparkling flecks of Pyrite, or fool's gold, adding to its mystical allure.

Arguably, the finest Lapis Lazuli is a dark royal blue color and as with all gems, the quality of its cutting is also a consideration.

MALACHITE

Malachite is named after the Greek word "moloche," meaning mallow, due to its similarity in color to mallow leaves.

A secondary copper mineral, Malachite is a popular gem that has light and dark vivid green banded areas. Many beautiful specimens of Malachite contain special combinations with other minerals, such as Azurite, Cuprite or Chrysocolla.

Legends and lore

Malachite was admired by ancient Greek followers of the goddess Venus and thought to possess great powers.

In Rome, it was called the "peacock stone" and dedicated to the goddess Juno, who protects against lightning and other perils of nature. Continuing these ancient traditions, to this day some Italians wear Malachite as protection against the evil eye.

Popular with the ancient Egyptians, according to legend, their hippo goddess Toeris (also associated with Hathor) wore a necklace of many beads including Malachite.

According to legend, it was worn to detect impending danger, and was believed to break into pieces when danger was near. Hence, it was often regarded as the guardian gem of travelers.

Malachite 14K Yellow Gold Ring

According to modern crystal healers its powers include protection, power, peace, hope, love, and success in business.

Just the facts

Malachite's banded, light and dark green designs are unique and give it a visual appearance unlike any other gem. The light and dark green bands are so distinctive that it is arguably one of the most easily recognizable gemstones.

Its ability to mix with other minerals has lead to Malachite being unearthed in a wide array of attractive colors and patterns. These unique combinations create some intriguing gemstones.

Malachite & White Topaz 14K Yellow Gold Ring

Malachite

MALACHITE:	Also know as the Peacock Stone
Origins:	Namibia, Tanzania & Zambia
Colors Found:	Banded light & dark green
Family:	Malachite
Hardness:	3.50 - 4.00
Refractive Index:	1.85
Relative Density:	3.90 - 4.00

MOONSTONE

Popular with the Romans, who thought it was formed out of moonlight, and in India, where it is considered a sacred zodiac gem, Moonstone is one of the most coveted varieties of Feldspar. Other names for Moonstone include Adularia (a variety found in the European Alps near the Adula Group) and Selenite (from the Greek "selene," meaning moon).

Legend and lore

Laced with superstitions, suspicion, humor and romance, the earliest known traditions describe Moonstone as having been set in the forehead of a four-handed Indian god who represented the moon. Partly from its unique color, partly from a superstition that represented it as feeling the influence of the deity whom it adorned, it first gained the name by which it continues to be known today in ancient India.

The gem's modern western roots allegedly originate from the German word "mondstein," (Moonstone) that was used to describe a lustrous variety of Feldspar in the late 18th century.

Sri Lankan Rainbow Moonstone
14K Yellow Gold Ring

This gem has always been revered because of its lunar attraction. In antiquity, Moonstone was believed to be the solidified rays of the moon and the glimmering light within was thought to be the light of the good spirit that lived within the gem. In ancient Rome, Moonstones were thought to change their appearance depending on the waning phases of the moon. They also thought that a picture of Diana, the goddess of the moon, could be seen in every Moonstone.

In the Middle Ages, people thought that if you fell into a deep sleep after gazing into a Moonstone it would tell you the future. It has always been considered a feminine or "Goddess" gem. One Asian legend points out that where there is a moon there is no rain and so the name Moonstone means "no tears."

Sri Lankan Rainbow Moonstone & White Topaz
14K White Gold Ring

Moonstone is a highly prized gift for lovers as it is believed to arouse tender passion. According to another legend, a Moonstone placed in the mouth while the moon is full gives lovers the power to read their futures together. In antiquity, men used Moonstone to predict the future by placing them in their mouths.

A symbol of the Third Eye, Moonstone was once believed to balance yin/yang, protect against epilepsy and sun stroke, cure headaches and nose bleeds, and ensure a high yield in crops. Today, crystal healers

Sri Lankan Rainbow Moonstone
14K Yellow Gold Ring

believe that it can help men open their feminine emotional aspects. In some cultures, it is also believed to accentuate the wearer's nature, whether positive or negative.

MOONSTONE

Just the facts

Moonstone is a potassium-rich orthoclase member of the Feldspar group of minerals and is closely related to Sunstone and Labradorite. The name Feldspar comes from the German "feldt spat," meaning "field stone." This is because when Feldspar weathers, it releases large amounts of plant nutrients, such as potassium, which enrich the soil.

Moonstone shows a blue-whitish opalescence called "adularescence" (sometimes described as a "billowy" light or shimmer) that glides over the surface of the gem. Interference phenomena, due to the intergrowth of two different types of Feldspar with different refractive indexes, from the gem's layered structure are the cause of this effect. Moonstones are often cut as cabochons to maximize this effect.

Traditionally, Moonstone has a silver to blue sheen, a transparent to translucent to opaque clarity and a colorless body color. Sri Lankan Rainbow Moonstone possesses all these qualities and as it is quite rare and becoming rarer, it is definitely a "must have" for any jewelry collection. Sri Lankan Rainbow Moonstone is laboriously chipped directly from a host deposit in Meetiyaguda, Sri Lanka. Interestingly, Sri Lankan Rainbow Moonstone typically displays such a stunning transparent clarity (not usually associated with this gemstone), intense bright blue shimmer and dazzling iridescence (the rainbow-like color effect seen in some gems caused by cracks or structural layers breaking up light into spectral colors) that it can be cut as a faceted gemstone. This is truly unique and further accentuates the desirability of this highly collectible exotic gemstone.

Tanzanian Moonstone is a relatively new variety sourced from the Arusha region of Tanzania (the same region as Tanzanite).

Sri Lankan Rainbow Moonstone 14K White Gold Ring

Sri Lankan Rainbow Moonstone

MOONSTONE:	June's birthstone
Origins:	Brazil, India, Madagascar, Sri Lanka & Tanzania
Colors Found:	Colorless to brown, green, gray, pink, rainbow & yellow
Family:	Feldspar
Hardness:	6.00-6.50
Refractive Index:	1.51-1.57
Relative Density:	2.56-2.62

79

"As a gift for lovers the Moonstone takes a high rank, for it is believed to arouse the tender passion."

George Frederick Kunz

MORGANITE

Morganite, or Pink Beryl as it was initially described, was discovered in Madagascar in 1911. It was Tiffany's celebrated gemologist, George Frederick Kunz who renamed this unique gemstone in homage to the New York banker and his benefactor, John Pierpont Morgan.

Legends and lore

While Morganite has had little time to generate myths and legends, aside from their obvious physical beauty, all pink gemstones are believed by some to possess potent metaphysical properties connected with love and compassion.

Just the facts

Morganite, a member of the Beryl family and sister gem to Aquamarine and Emerald, is colored by trace amounts of manganese that find their way into the Beryl crystal structure. Morganite is found as flat, tabular crystals that resemble Rose Quartz, but they are easily differentiated by their luster and brilliance.

Morganite & White Topaz 14K Yellow Gold Ring

When Mother Nature created Morganite she made the ideal gemstone to complement all complexions. Coming in pinks from subtle lavenders to hot fuchsias and even pastel pink apricot blends (as typified by Medina Morganite and Magnolia Morganite), Morganite exudes charm and tenderness. Putting a unique twist on fashionable pink, Morganite provides the perfect antidote to the stress of modern life.

Its durability, luster, clarity, brilliance and myriad of beautiful pink hues, makes Morganite immensely suitable as a jewelry gemstone, appropriate for everyday wear. The only factor impeding Morganite's popularity is its scarcity.

Morganite 18K Yellow Gold Pendant

Morganite

MORGANITE:	Pink variety of Beryl
Origins:	Madagascar
Colors Found:	Pink
Family:	Beryl
Hardness:	7.50-8.00
Refractive Index:	1.57-1.60
Relative Density:	2.71-2.90

MOTHER OF PEARL

Mother of Pearl 925 Silver Bracelet

Mother of Pearl

MOTHER OF PEARL:	Ancient gemstone
Origins:	China & Japan
Colors Found:	Various
Family:	Organics
Hardness:	3.00-4.50
Refractive Index:	1.52-1.65
Relative Density:	2.60-2.80

While Queen Elizabeth I gave Mother of Pearl its name in the 15th century, the beauty of Mother of Pearl was used in the decoration of jewelry and ornaments 3,000 years before the birth of Christ. Also known as nacre (from the Arabic word for shell "naqqarah"), the name reflects the fact that these shells are the "mother" from which Pearls are created.

Mother of Pearl is the smooth lining of iridescent luster found in some mollusk shells such as oysters, abalone, mussels and paua shells.

Legends and lore

In the 1920's, a series of tombs were excavated to the east of Babylon in the Middle East. The tombs were of Sumerian royalty from ancient Mesopotamia and yielded a treasure of gold, silver and gemstones, and several beautiful wooden ornaments and musical instruments inlaid with Mother of Pearl (a testament to the wealth and sophistication of this ancient culture). The silver lyre of Ur, found in one of the graves in the royal cemetery, dates to between 2600 and 2400 BC. The lyre was entirely covered in sheet silver and inlaid with Mother of Pearl.

In Asia, centuries before the birth of Christ, the Chinese learned that beads or tiny figures of deities slipped between the soft mantle and the shell of a living mollusk soon became coated with Mother of Pearl. These beads and carvings were then taken to temples and offered to the gods in the hope that they would bestow good luck.

The Yaqui Indians of Mexico, immortalized in the shamanic tales of Carlos Castaneda, wear a necklace called the "hopo'orosim." The necklace is made of Mother of Pearl and is believed to provide the wearer with protection from evil.

By the 15th century Europe's growing demand for Mother of Pearl for use in gold and silver rings, necklaces and brooches had all but depleted the supplies of Mother of Pearl in the Persian Gulf.

In 1568 the Solomon Islands, known as "the Pearl of the Pacific," were discovered by the Spanish explorer Alvaro de Mendana. On discovering the island's rich bounty of gold and Mother of Pearl, he gave the archipelago its current name, believing that he had found the mythical source of King Solomon's mines.

MOTHER OF PEARL

In Polynesian lore, the iridescence of Mother of Pearl is attributed to the spirits of coral and sand, Okana and Uaro, who as legend has it, adorned Tahitian oysters in glistening cloaks covered in all the colors of the fish of the sea.

Just the facts

High quality Mother of Pearl is produced by the members of mollusk family called bivalves (two part shells).

Mother of Pearl's nacre forms when an organic particle becomes trapped within the mollusk or if the mollusk is injured in some way.

Sensing the object or damage, the living organism within the mollusk secretes calcium carbonate, a derivative mineral of aragonite, and the binding protein conchiolin. The layers of calcium carbonate settle and are interspersed by the conchiolin, which acts as a kind of organic glue binding the crystals together.

Mother of Pearl is created by a living organism and thus environmental factors play a crucial role in its formation. As Mother of Pearl producing mollusks cannot regulate their body temperature, they are susceptible to changes in external conditions. Mother of Pearl appears in a wide variety of colors and derives its color from its genetic make-up and the water in which it grows.

OBSIDIAN

This gem is supposedly named after Obsidian, a Roman said to have brought the first gems from Lake Shalla, Ethiopia to Rome.

Legends and lore

Obsidian is regarded as one of the most important "teachers" of the New Age movement. Obsidian is said to sharpen both external and internal vision. For some crystal healers, it is the warrior of truth and shows the self where the ego is at, and what we must change in order to advance to the next step of evolutionary growth.

Just the facts

Obsidian is formed by the rapid cooling of viscous lava due to volcanic explosions. It is made of the same minerals as granite but cools so quickly that they do not have time to crystallize.

Obsidian has a glassy luster and is usually black or a very dark green, but it can also be found in an almost colorless form.

Obsidian may be fashioned into a razor sharp cutting edge and ancient civilizations used it for jewelry, mirrors, arrowheads, spearheads, scrapers and cutting tools, such as the sacrificial knives of the Aztecs. Because of this, Obsidian has been found in locations far from its original source. This might have confused a few gemologists but it has helped us understand more about the travels of our ancestors.

Today, transparent specimens are faceted, usually into step cuts, while less transparent pieces are fashioned into cabochons.

Especially prized in jewelry, Snowflake Obsidian is a striking black, lustrous opaque gem with white bold markings, formed by internal bubbles or crystals of potassium feldspar, much like beautiful patterns of snowflakes on a black background.

Snowflake Obsidian 925 Silver Necklace

OBSIDIAN:	Natural glass of volcanic origin
Origins:	Mexico & US
Colors Found:	Almost clear, black & very dark green
Family:	Obsidian
Hardness:	5.50-7.00
Refractive Index:	1.48-1.53
Relative Density:	2.33-2.60

Snowflake Obsidian

ONYX

Onyx is a Chalcedony Quartz with a fine texture and parallel bands of alternate colors. Commonly known as "black magic," this gem's name comes from the Greek word "Onyx," which means fingernail or claw. Legend says that one day while Venus was sleeping Cupid cut her fingernails and left the clippings scattered on the ground. Because no part of a heavenly body can die, the gods turned them into a gem, which later became known as Onyx.

Legends and lore

Related to its mythological origin, Onyx is believed by some to encourage the growth of fingernails, hair and skin. In Greek times, almost all colors of Chalcedony Quartz from fingernail white to dark brown and black were called Onyx. Later, the Romans narrowed the term to refer to black and dark brown colors only. Today when we think of Onyx we often preface the word with "black" to distinguish it from other varieties of Onyx that come in white, reddish brown, green, brown and banded colors. Onyx which is reddish brown and white is known as Sardonyx.

With its consecutive layers of different colors, the ancient Romans believed Onyx to be an excellent cameo (a gem carved in relief) gemstone. Sardonyx was highly valued in Rome, especially for seals, because it was said never to stick to the wax. Roman General Publius Cornelius Scipio was known for wearing lots of Sardonyx.

Onyx is often associated with instincts and intuition. It is believed to give one the power to deeply analyze a situation before reacting to it, as well as better business acumen and management skills. Crystal healers also believe that it restores confidence in life and love, thereby increasing your happiness.

Just the facts

Quartz gemstones are commonly separated into two groups based on the size of their individual crystals. The macrocrystalline Quartz (large crystal) group includes many popular gemstones such as Amethyst, Ametrine and Citrine. Cryptocrystalline Quartz includes species whose individual crystals are too small to be easily distinguished. Apart from being a variety within the group, Chalcedony is also a catchall term to describe cryptocrystalline Quartz and includes many gems that have been coveted since antiquity.

Black Onyx 925 Silver Necklace

ONYX:	Also known as Black Magic
Origins:	Brazil, India, Madagascar & Uruguay
Colors Found:	Black & white
Family:	Chalcedony Quartz
Hardness:	6.50
Refractive Index:	1.54
Relative Density:	2.59-2.61

OPAL

One of the world's most coveted gemstones, Opal's name evolved from the Roman word "opalus" from the Greek word "opallios," meaning "to see a change of color." The Greek word was a modification of the ancient Indian Sanskrit name for Opal, "upala," which meant "precious stone." If one spoke in mixed tongues, then Opal would be opallios upala, "to see a change of color precious stone."

While their body color covers a broad spectrum, Opals are most prized for their unique fiery play of color, reflecting and refracting light into flashes of multiple colors.

Legends and lore

Historically, Opal was considered a lucky charm that brought beauty, success and happiness to its wearer. The early Greeks believed Opals embodied the powers of foresight and prophecy.

Lightning Ridge Black Opal & White Topaz 14K Yellow Gold Ring

The Romans also cherished Opals, considering them to be a symbol of hope and purity - an appropriate attribute for a gem with a rainbow locked within it!

The Arabs thought that Opals must have fallen from heaven in flashes of lightning. According to Arab tradition, it is believed that Opals prevent lightening strikes, shield its wearer from any undesirable elements in their day-to-day lives and give a cloak of invisibility to its wearer when desired.

Opal featured in literature with Shakespeare referring to it in "Twelfth Night" as "the queen of gems."

The history books would have us believe that the European supplies of Opal came from India and the Middle East, but it is far more likely that they came from Hungarian mines.

Cherry Fire Opal 14K Yellow Gold Ring

Opal made the headlines in the 1890's with the first samples of Australian Opal. The Hungarians declared that the new Australian variety was not the real thing, as Opals with such a fusion of fire and color had never been seen before. According to Koori (indigenous Australians) legend, the Creator came down to Earth on a rainbow to bring a message of peace to all humans. At the spot where his feet touched the ground, the stones became alive and started sparkling in all the colors of the rainbow, giving birth to Australian Opals. Today, Opals are one of Australia's national treasures and one of the world's most prized gemstones.

Lightning Ridge Black Opal

Queen Victoria intervened in the near destruction of the 19th century Opal market when the writer Sir

"There is in them a softer fire than the Ruby, there is the brilliant purple of the Amethyst, and the sea green of the Emerald - all shining together in incredible union. Some by their splendor rival the colors of the painters, others the flame of burning sulfur or of fire quickened by oil."

Pliny the Elder

OPAL

Lightning Ridge Black Opal 14K Yellow Gold Ring

*Andamooka Semi Black Opal & White Topaz
14K Yellow Gold Ring*

African Fire Opal

Walter Scott started a superstition that Opals were bad luck for people not born in October. In one of his novels, the heroine owned an Opal that burned fiery red when she was angry and turned ashen gray upon her death. Queen Victoria finally dispelled the curse by giving Opal jewelry as gifts at a royal wedding.

Scandinavian women still wear Opal hair bands to ward off the onset of gray hair, while some people believe that this gemstone has therapeutic properties that rejuvenate the inner spirit and invigorate the mind.

Just the facts

Opals possess flashes of rainbow colors that change with the angle of observation, called "play of color." This effect is similar to the rainbow colors displayed on a soap bubble, only much more dramatic. This should not be confused with "opalescence," which is the milky blue or pearly appearance of Opal caused by the reflection of light.

The physical structure of Opal is unique. Tiny precipitated spheres of silicon dioxide form a pyramid shaped grid interspersed with water. Tiny natural faults in this grid cause the characteristic play of color.

Opals are typically classified depending on the "potch" (the host rock, also called the "matrix") on which the Opal is formed and their resulting transparency. For example, Black Opal has a black potch, Semi Black Opal has a potch darker than gray, but not quite black, White Opal has a white potch, Queensland Boulder Opal is Opal with an ironstone (boulder) potch and Jelly Opal (also know as Crystal Opal) is Opal with no potch whatsoever. Distinguished from Jelly Opal by its minimal play of color, Fire Opal is Jelly Opal that displays extraordinary fiery yellows, tangerines and reds. Matrix Opal (also know as "opal with matrix") are any Opals where the potch or matrix is visible face up.

Opal actually exhibits many different colors including cherry colored specimens that rival Ruby, fiery-orange Opals that sparkle like Spessartite Garnet, tropical blue gems as intense as Chalcedony, and even gorgeous pinks and greens.

Today approximately 95% of the world's Opal is sourced from a handful of prominent mining areas in Australia, namely Lightning Ridge, Coober Pedy, Andamooka and Mintabe.

Black Opal

Black Opal is principally found at Lightning Ridge in New South Wales, Australia. Known as the "King of Opals," Lightning Ridge Black Opal has been coveted since it was discovered in 1902. Located 575 miles north of Sydney, Lightning Ridge (a free wheeling town of about 15,000 people) is the world's major source of the finest Black Opal.

This magnificent gemstone is the most coveted form of Opal. Its dark background color sets the spectral colors ablaze much like a storm cloud behind a rainbow (the black background provides contrast and intensity to this Opal's play of color). So prized is Black Opal that even wafer thin slices are made into doublets or triplets to give them enough strength and depth to set into gold rings and other jewelry items.

The Black Opal mining fields of Lightning Ridge and the majority of Australia's Opal fields are located in a geological phenomenon called "The Great Australian Basin." The basin was formed from sediments of a large inland sea that existed over 140 million years ago. Approximately 120 million years later, sandstones were deposited by waterways over the top of these sedimentary rocks. Eventually these younger rocks weathered, and their silica filtered down to cavities in the older host rock in the form of a gel. The silica gel hardened forming around a nucleus, creating the Opal's characteristic regular spheres and voids. It's the diffraction of light through these transparent spaces that produce Opal's brilliant play of colors.

Lightning Ridge Black Opal 14K Yellow Gold Ring

Mined directly from narrow seams in sedimentary rock, Opal mining involves hard digging with picks and shovels 20-59 feet underground. Buckets are then loaded and hauled to the surface using simple mechanical winches. The rough Opal (called "nobbies") is initially separated by hand, prior to sieving. The remaining Opal nobbies are then taken to small converted cement mixers to wash off the excess dirt.

Lightning Ridge Black Opal 14K Yellow Gold Ring

Unfortunately, all Australian Opal, but especially those from Lightning Ridge, are becoming increasingly scarce. The old fields at Lightning Ridge that produced high dome cabochons are virtually depleted, with only marginal areas presently being worked. Despite the fact that the government has opened many new prospective areas, to date there have been no significant new prospects found. Opal production at Lightning Ridge is half of what it was 10 years ago. The current supply problems are

Cherry Fire Opal

89

OPALL

Fire Opal 14K Yellow Gold Ring

Queensland Boulder Opal 14K Yellow Gold Pendant

Queensland Boulder Opal

infuriating as international demand remains high. The present jewelry trends favoring color have seen an increase in Opal use among the world's leading jewelry houses.

Boulder Opal

Boulder Opal is found sparsely distributed over a wide area of Australian ironstone or boulder country where the Opal (silica mix) fills veins, cracks, cavities and crevices in ironstone boulders. Opal bearing boulder is always cut to include the host brown ironstone. The GIA (Gemological Institute of America) classifies two types: gems with ironstone visible face up, called "opal with matrix" and gems with no visible inclusions, called "opal in matrix." Boulder Opal is usually cut as "opal with matrix" to the contours of the Opal vein, creating a baroque wavy surface often freeform and irregular in shape, making each Boulder Opal unique. Located northwest of Lightning Ridge in western Queensland, the Queensland Boulder Opal Fields encompass a vast area centering on the town of Quilpie and extending as far north as Winton and south to Cunamulla. The last 12 months have seen slightly lower production levels, with any fine gems quickly snapped up.

Known for its lively flaming bright rich colors, this variety is in very high demand and extremely popular. Interest in Queensland Boulder Opal has increased markedly over the last 20 years as this unique type of Opal gains recognition from gem enthusiasts the world over.

Fire Opal

Fire Opals are appropriately named for their fiery cherries, sunburst yellows and deep tangerines. Unique and mysterious, Fire Opal is remarkable in that unlike many other Opals its play of color is minimal. Also known as Mexican Opal, Mexican Fire Opal, Tanzanian Fire Opal, Cherry Fire Opal, Ethiopian Fire Opal, Brazilian Fire Opal or Sun Opal, its legendary popularity instead comes from its breathtaking brilliance, opalescence, extraordinary fiery hues and stunning clarity. Fire Opals have been treasured in the Americas since the time of the Aztecs, where they were named "Quetzalitzlipyollitli" or "gemstone of the bird of paradise." Coveted by the Aztecs as symbols of intense love, such radiant gemstones were believed to have emerged from the

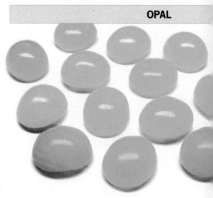

OPAL

primordial waters of creation. While Fire Opal is predominately sourced from Mexico (and occasionally Australia), this gem has recently been found in Tanzania, Ethiopia, Mali and now Brazil. While Opal has been mined in Brazil since approximately 1945, production has always been very limited, making it difficult to secure commercial quantities. Today, the Piaui State is increasingly garnering international acclaim for its Opals, with their quality favorably compared to Australian Opals, arguably the world's finest. With the enforcement of new mining regulations, scarcity has increased, strengthening the appeal of this relatively new addition to the Opal family.

Green Opal

Discovered in the 1960's, Green Opal is a green translucent Opal that resembles Chrysoprase or Jade and is commonly called Prase Opal or Chrysopal because of its resemblance to Chrysoprase. It is mined in the Arusha region of Tanzania (the same region as Tanzanite). While this gem does not display the play of color found in some Opals, its mint to apple green body color has made it very popular for jewelry. Trace amounts of nickel gives this Opal its unique color.

Cherry Fire Opal 14K White Gold Ring

Jelly Opal

Jelly Opal (also known as Water Opal or Crystal Opal) is predominately mined in Mexico. Offering an attractive blend of indistinct colors, it is transparent pure Opal with a gelatinous appearance and an occasionally pronounced opalescence (bluish sheen). The play of color is a subtle sheen dancing throughout the gem, rather than distinct color patches. When held out in direct light, Jelly Opal can display some of the most intense Opal colors. Very occasionally it is also found in Lightning Ridge, Australia, where it is essentially Black Opal without the black potch background. This is the type of Opal used in Opal inlay jewelry that has the base of the setting blackened (typically using Black Rhodium) before a precisely cut crystal Opal is set within.

Brazilian Fire Opal & White Topaz 14K Yellow Gold Ring

Peruvian Opal

Hailing from the Andes and coveted by the ancient Incas, Peruvian Opal is extremely rare and exhibits an exquisite translucent coloring. While it typically

Green Opal & Blue Diamond 14K Yellow Gold Pendant

91

OPAL

Pink Opal 14K Yellow Gold Ring

Andamooka Semi Black Opal 14K Yellow Gold Ring

OPAL:	October's birthstone
Origins:	Australia, Brazil, Ethiopia, Indonesia, Mexico, Peru, South Africa, Tanzania & Zimbabwe
Colors Found:	Various
Family:	Opal
Hardness:	5.50-6.50
Refractive Index:	1.33-1.46
Relative Density:	1.80-2.30

comes in blue or pink colors, greens are also occasionally found.

Semi Black Opal

With a brighter transparency than Black Opal, Semi Black Opal has a body color darker than gray, but not quite black. Opacity is the key that divides black from semi black with Black Opal appearing more opaque than Semi Black Opal. Semi Black Opal was discovered at Andamooka in the 1930's. Situated 398 miles north by road from Adelaide, South Australia, Andamooka remains a typical dusty "wild west" desert town. In the 1960's when Andamooka was booming, an Opal setting (at the time worth hundreds of thousands of dollars) was presented to Queen Elizabeth II. While Andamooka Opals remain world renowned, only a small amount of Opal is now mined from Andamooka due to high logistical expenses related to its remoteness. Andamooka Opal is typically of an exceptionally high quality, but has become more difficult to source in the last few years. Andamooka is reportedly very quiet at present with less than 50 serious miners.

White Opal

White Opal is translucent with a creamy appearance that dominates the diffracted colors. While all the Australian Opal fields produce White Opal, the majority is mined in Coober Pedy.

Commenting that "there is in them a softer fire than the Ruby, there is the brilliant purple of the Amethyst, and the sea green of the Emerald - all shining together in incredible union," Opal clearly impressed Pliny the Elder (23-79 AD), Roman historian and author of the Historia Naturalis, the world's first encyclopedia. With only 25% of mined Opal finding its way into jewelry, if you're looking to be impressed with Opals, there is no better place to start building your Opal collection than at GemsTV!

Andamooka Semi Black Opal

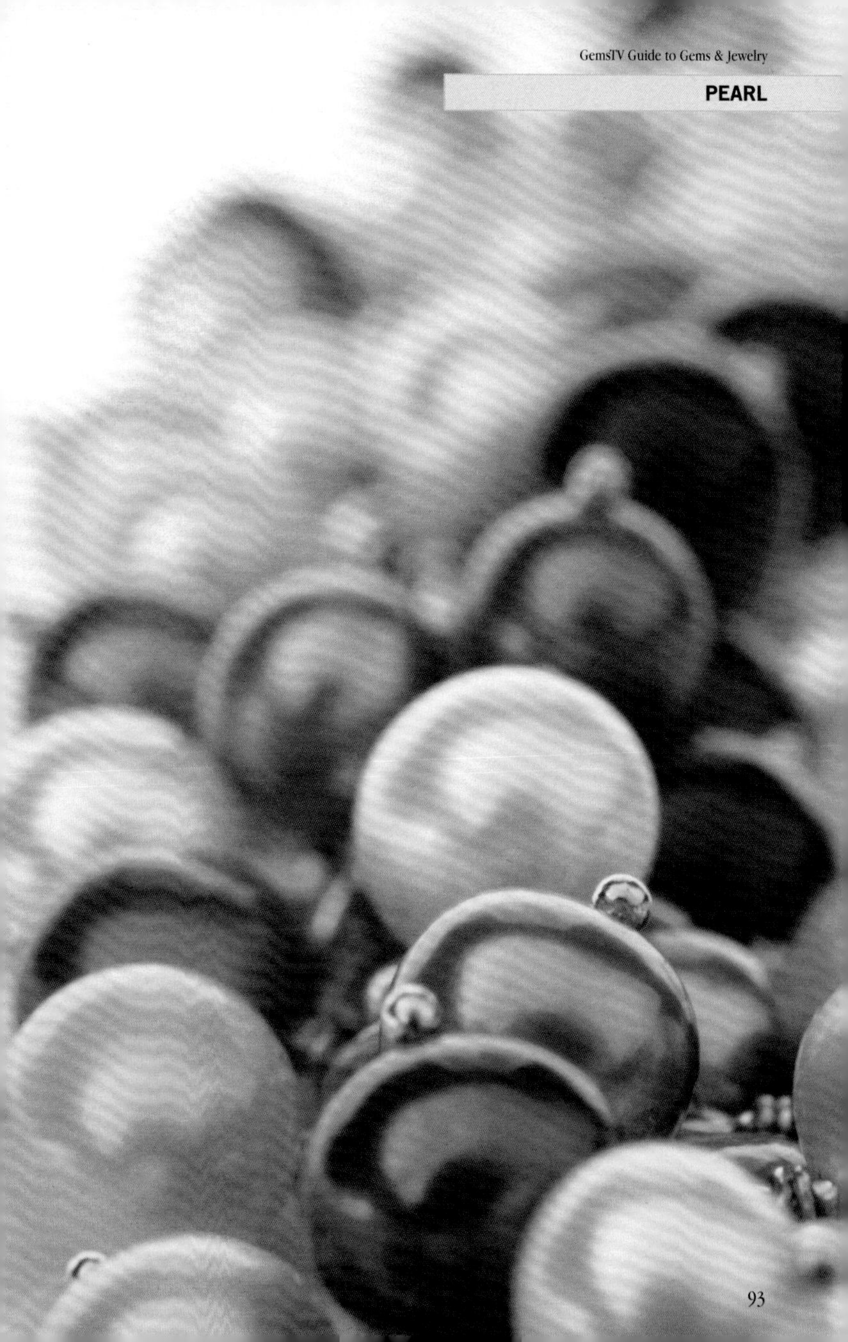

PEARL

Freshwater Pearl 14K Yellow Gold Ring

Chinese Freshwater Pearls in their clam

Pearls are one of the oldest known gems and for centuries were considered the most valuable. So valuable if fact, that the Roman General Vitellius allegedly financed an entire military campaign with just one of his mother's Pearl earrings!

Thankfully, the days of island inhabitants free diving into azure oceans to harvest Pearls are more or less over. The lust for uncultured Pearls once decimated entire species of mollusks, relegating this gem of the sea to the elite few. Today, thanks to the innovations of Japanese noodle maker, Kokichi Mikimoto (the man who perfected Pearl farming and who convinced the world to accept them), these fragile ecosystems are now safe, with natural uncultured Pearls usually appearing only as antiques.

Legends and lore

The Romans were particularly enamored of this gem of the sea. Rome's Pearl craze reached its zenith during the 1st century BC when upper class Roman women (the lower ranks were forbidden from wearing them) wore their Pearls to bed so they could be reminded of their wealth immediately upon awakening. They also sewed so many into their gowns that they actually walked on their Pearl-encrusted hems. The famously excessive Emperor Caligula, having made his beloved horse a Consul, decorated it with a Pearl necklace.

A lover of luxury, Julius Caesar, apart from his well known military accomplishments, was also an expert in Pearls and could reportedly accurately ascertain their value by simply weighing them in his hand.

Cleopatra flaunted her enormous wealth and power during a competition with Marc Anthony to see who could host the most lavish dinner party. She allegedly crushed a Pearl from one of her earrings into a glass of wine to demonstrate to Marc Anthony how she could drink the wealth of nations.

The first known source of Pearls was the Persian Gulf and the ancients of the area believed that Pearls were a symbol of the moon and had magical powers. Indeed, the oldest known Pearl jewelry is a necklace found in the sarcophagus of a Persian princess who died in 520 BC.

The earliest written record of their value is in the "Shu King," a 23 BC Chinese book in which the scribe sniffs that a lesser king sent tribute of "strings of Pearls not quite round." The Chinese also used Pearls in medicinal ways to cure eye ailments, heart trouble, indigestion, fever and bleeding. To this day Pearl powder is still popular in China as a skin whitener and cosmetic.

In India, Pearls were believed to give peace of mind and strengthen the body and soul.

In antiquity, it was thought that swallowing whole or powdered Pearls cured matters of the mind and heart, strengthened nerves and even improved virility.

The Koran states that a good Muslim, upon entering the Kingdom of Heaven, "is crowned with Pearls of incomparable luster, and is attended by beautiful maidens resembling hidden Pearls."

While Queen Isabella had to hock her impressive collection of jewelry to fund Christopher Columbus' expedition to discover the New World, the investment paid off as the discovery of Pearls in Central American waters added to the wealth of Spain. The flood of American Pearls onto the European market earned the newly discovered continent the nickname "land of Pearls." Unfortunately, greed and lust for these gems of the sea resulted in the depletion of virtually all the American Pearl oyster populations by the 17th century.

During the Dark Ages, while fair maidens of nobility cherished delicate Pearl necklaces, gallant knights often wore Pearls onto the battlefield. They believed that the magic possessed by the lustrous gems would protect them from harm.

Pearls have long been considered ideal wedding gifts because they symbolize purity and innocence. In the Hindu religion, the presentation of an un-drilled Pearl and its piercing has formed part of the marriage ceremony. In the West, Pearls are the recommended gift for couples celebrating their 3rd and 30th wedding anniversaries.

Just the facts

The Pearl begins life as a foreign body (a grain of sand, coral or parasite), which makes its way into the shell of a marine or freshwater mollusk – usually oysters or clams. The mollusk's defense mechanism starts to coat the intruder with layers of a slightly iridescent substance, "nacre" (from the Arabic word for shell "naqqarah"), which is the attractive outside of the Pearl. In its natural environment this will, after many years, form a Pearl that is of a significant size and quality.

Freshwater Pearl 14K Yellow Gold Ring

Freshwater Pearl & Diamond 14K Yellow Gold Pendant

Tahitian Pearl & Diamond 14K Yellow Gold Ring

PEARL

Freshwater Pearl & White Topaz 14K Yellow Gold Ring

Unlike natural Pearls, cultivated Pearls do not begin as accidental intruders. First cultivated by the Chinese as early as the 12th Century, the process starts with "nucleation." A cultivated Pearl usually begins its life when a spherical bead or a piece of mantle tissue is placed inside the mollusk. After this seeding process, the Pearl farmers place the mollusks in wire-mesh baskets and suspend them in water. The aqua-culturists carefully tend to the mollusks, overseeing their development for 18 months to 5 years. The depth of the nacre coating, an important factor in determining the color of Pearls, depends on how long the seeded Pearls are left in place before being harvested. Usually, only half of the Pearls will be marketable and less than 10% of these will be top-quality. While Pearls are classified as colored gems, there is a unique appeal about them. Unlike other gemstones that are born of earth and fire, Pearls are waterborn organic gems that originate from living animals. They are also unique in the sense that the principals of the 4 C's (color, cut, clarity and carat weight) cannot be applied to them. The evaluation of Pearls requires a different set of criteria. A Pearl is appraised according to the display of color, luster, surface clarity, shape and size.

Pearl's two colors

The body colors themselves can be white, cream, pink, rose, golden, silver, gray and black. As color preference is subjective, there is no such thing as a bad body color - it is purely a matter of choice. Apart from the obvious body color, there is actually a second color to consider when evaluating Pearls. This second color is actually a result of subtle iridescence. While not instantly obvious, especially when similar to the body color, this effect lends Pearls much of their allure. Typically, this iridescence is seen most strongly on the crest of a Pearl's horizon. This beautiful, shimmering effect is known as the "orient" or overtone and denotes the depth of the nacre. Pearls with rich colorful orients are generally more coveted than those that have little or no orient.

*Freshwater Pearl & White Topaz
14K Rose Gold Earrings*

PEARL

Pearl luster

Pearls are bright, reflective gemstones. While Pearls with clean and even surfaces reflect more light than Pearls with blemished surfaces, please remember that as a natural creation, like inclusions in mineral gems, most Pearls do have blemishes.

Intelligent jewelers solve this problem by concealing blemishes near the drill holes.

Weight and size

As with other gemstones, value and size are intrinsically linked. The bigger the Pearl the more desirable it becomes. However, there is one important difference: Pearls are measured and expressed by their size, not weight (e.g., 8.5 millimeters).

Pearl locations

As with all things natural, Pearls can only grow in the right conditions. Different Pearl varieties from different locations command different prices. The best quality Pearls are found in the waters of French Polynesia, Japan and China. However, due to the different environments, mollusk species and farming techniques, all cultivated Pearls have their own distinctive qualities. The three main Pearl varieties on GemsTV are Freshwater Pearls, Tahitian Pearls and South Sea Pearls.

Freshwater Pearls

Although historically originating in Japan, China is now a major producer of Freshwater Pearls. Our Chinese Freshwater Pearls are farmed in the Fuchum, Wu and Ling Rivers of the Zhejiang province in southern China. China has successfully concentrated on Freshwater Pearls using not oysters but freshwater clams. The humble clam, while not as widely celebrated as its cousin the oyster, is equally capable of producing high-quality Pearls.

Tahitian Pearls

Tahitian Pearls are from French Polynesia and are named after the tropical island of Tahiti. Grown in the large black-lipped saltwater oyster (Pinctada Margaritifera), Tahitian Pearls are celebrated for their exceptional beauty.

Freshwater Pearl 925 Silver Necklace

97

PEARL

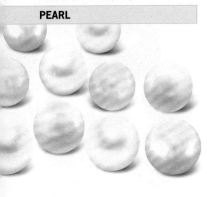

Freshwater Pearl & Diamond 14K Yellow Gold Ring

Freshwater and Tahitian Pearls

PEARL:	June's birthstone
Origins:	Australia, China, Indonesia, Japan, Philippines & Tahiti
Colors Found:	Black, cream, gold, golden yellow, gray, orange, pink, silver & white
Family:	Organics
Hardness:	3.00 - 4.00
Refractive Index:	1.53 - 1.68
Relative Density:	2.60 - 2.78

Tahiti's pure and tranquil waters are the ideal cultivation grounds for the dramatic Tahitian Pearl.

Tahitian legend says that Te Ufi (Pinctada Margaritifera) was given to man by Oro, the god of peace and fertility, who came to earth on a rainbow and offered the Pearl to the beautiful princess Bora Bora as a sign of eternal love.

First appearing in Europe in 1845, Napoleon III's wife, Empress Eugenie was responsible for bringing Tahitian Pearls into fashion. After the fall of Napoleon, Empress Eugenie's necklace was auctioned at Christies for $20,000. "Ezra" was the most famous natural Tahitian Pearl, the centerpiece of a necklace that was part of the Russian crown jewels.

Tahitian Black Pearls are prized and admired throughout the world. The first Pearl farms were established on the atoll of Hikueru and the island of Bora Bora in the early 1960's. Exports began in 1972 and production was subsequently expanded on the islands of Marutea Sud and Mangareva. Today, Tahitian Black Pearls are cultivated in Pearl farms in a sprawling group of atolls and islands in French Polynesia, primarily the lagoons of the Tuamotu-Gambier Archipelago.

Tahitian Pearls generally range in size from 8 millimeters to 16 millimeters and consist of many thousands of layers of Aragonite (a variety of calcium carbonate). In contrast to many other Pearl varieties, Tahitian Pearls are cultured for 4-5 years and have a nacre thickness of 3-10 millimeters.

Tahitian Pearls display a shimmering orient that is green, blue, pink or violet in color. These orient colors are in striking contrast to their silver to black body color. Their orient or overtone colors are sometimes given specific names (deep green is called "fly wing," "peacock" for the combination of green and pink, and "eggplant" is a dark toned body color combined with pink).

South Sea Pearls

Highly coveted, South Sea Pearls come from Australia, Indonesia and the Philippines. Cultured in varieties of Pinctada Maxima, this large, warm-water loving, gold and silver-lipped oyster produces Pearls of fabulous colors.

PERIDOT

Shining with a bright green glow even at night, Peridot was called the "gem of the sun" by the ancient Egyptians and the "evening emerald" by Romans. Peridot was a favorite gemstone of Cleopatra and was historically mistaken for Emerald. The pronunciation of this popular gem is often confused and should be pronounced "Pair-ee-doh" as opposed to "Pair-ee-dot."

Peridot's name origin is uncertain, but several theories exist. Some sources speculate that it comes from the 13th century Middle English word "peridote," meaning "bright spot" or "bright button," an apt description for this gem given its brilliance. Other sources attribute it to the French "peritot," meaning "unclear," probably due to its silky appearance. While some sources suggest the word Peridot comes from the Greek "peridona," indicating plentiful, this seems unlikely as this gem was scarce even in classical times. Given the ancient source of Peridot, the most likely candidate is the Arabic word "faridat," which simply means "gem."

Legends and lore

Popular in early Greek and Roman jewelry, Peridot has been coveted since 1500 BC when the Egyptians started mining it on Zeberget Island, later known as St. John's Island, about 50 miles off the Egyptian coast in the Red Sea. Interestingly, "zabargad" is the Arabic word for Peridot.

Peridot 14K White Gold Ring

Peridot mining was traditionally done at night when the gem's natural glow made it easier to spot. The ancient Egyptians even believed that Peridot became invisible under the sun's rays. They also believed that Peridot was colored by the golden glow of their sun god Ra, and was thus a powerful protector from harm.

Hawaiians believe Peridot is the goddess Pele's tears, while it is mentioned in the Bible (using its old name Chrysolite, meaning "golden stone" in Greek) as being one of the "stones of fire" (Ezekiel 28:13-16) that were given to Moses and set in the breastplate of Aaron (Exodus 28:15-30). Peridot is also one of the twelve gemstones set in the foundations of the city walls of Jerusalem (Revelations 21:19) and associated with the Apostle Bartholomew.

Peridot 14K Yellow Gold Ring

While Cleopatra reportedly had a fine collection of "Emerald" jewelry, it was in reality predominantly Peridot.

Peridot & White Topaz 14K White Gold Ring

PERIDOT

Peridot

Peridot 14K Yellow Gold Ring

PERIDOT:	August's birthstone
Origins:	China, Kenya, Pakistan, South Africa, Tanzania & US
Colors Found:	Green to yellowish green
Family:	Olivine
Hardness:	6.50
Refractive Index:	1.64 -1.69
Relative Density:	3.34

The Ottoman Sultans gathered the largest collection of Peridot during their 600-year reign from 1300-1918, with an impressive array of both loose gemstones as well as earrings, rings and other jewelry.

Powdered Peridot has been used to cure asthma and a Peridot placed under the tongue of someone in the grip of a fever was believed to lessen their thirst. Legend has it that drinking from a Peridot goblet can increase the potency of medicines.

Pirates believed Peridot had the power to drive away evil spirits (and the night's terrors), especially if set in gold. But as protection from evil spirits they believed it must be pierced, strung on donkey hair and worn on the left arm.

Possibly the most unusual Peridot is that which comes from meteorites called Pallasites, after their 1772 discoverer, a German scientist called Peter Simon Pallas. Some have even been faceted and set in jewelry, one of the few extraterrestrial gemstones known to man. In 2003 Peridot was discovered on Mars, making it the first gemstone to be discovered on another planet.

Just the facts

Peridot is the gem variety of Olivine and exhibits colors ranging from golden lime greens to rich grass greens. Traditionally, the most coveted color hues have been the rich grass greens. However, many Peridots with slight yellowish hues still exhibit attractive colors that are extremely popular. This once again demonstrates that your individual preference should always be the primary factor when collecting colored gemstones.

The elements that give gemstones their color are termed "idiochromatic" or "self colored" if they are an intrinsic ingredient of the gem (meaning the color results from a coloring element that is always incorporated into the crystal structure of the mineral) and "allochromatic" or "other colored" if they are trace elements (small amounts of an element that is not part of the normal crystal causes the color). In many gems, the major element in the chemical composition is colorless in a pure state such as Topaz or Sapphires. If these "allochromatic" gems occur in a variety of colors such as Ruby or Sapphire, then it is usually the result of trace elements. In the case of an "idiochromatic" gem like Peridot, the coloring

PERIDOT

element iron is actually part of the crystal, meaning the gem is always the same color (Peridot is always green).

Because of the way Peridot splits and bends light, it has an attractive velvety, silky appearance with a shining rich glow.

While the San Carlos Apache Reservation, Arizona has the world's largest gem quality Peridot deposit, China has recently become a major producer. In 1994, an exciting new deposit was discovered in Pakistan, producing some of the finest Peridot ever seen. The new mine is located 15,000 feet above sea level in the Nanga Parbat region in the far west of the Himalayan Mountains in the Pakistani part of Kashmir.

PEZZOTTAITE

Displaying gorgeous deep raspberry pinks, Pezzottaite is a relatively new gemstone that has been subject to much confusion due to its similarities with the Red variety of Beryl, Bixbite.

Just the Facts

Pezzottaite was discovered in November 2002 at the Sakavalana mine located about 87 miles southwest of Antsirabe in southern Madagascar. The initial deposit yielded some extremely rare large crystals and it is now practically depleted although small amounts are now mined elsewhere in Madagascar. The Sakavalana pegmatite where Pezzottaite was discovered was mined by the French for Tourmaline during the 1940's. The initial Pezzottaite deposit was discovered in a large crystal bearing cavity that also contained Tourmaline and Spodumene. Not surprisingly, Pezzottaite was initially mistakenly sold as Tourmaline in Madagascar.

Pezzottaite is mined from granitic pegmatites using hand tools, making its extraction slow and difficult.

Having a slightly different chemical composition to Bixbite ($Be_3Al_2Si_6O_{18}$), it was named Pezzottaite ($Cs[Be_2Li]Al_2Si_6O_{18}$) in September 2003 after Dr. Federico Pezzotta of the Museo Civico di Storia Naturale, Milan, Italy, in recognition of his contributions to the mineralogy of Madagascar.

Pezzottaite has a variety of trade names including Madagascan Raspberyl, Raspberyl and Raspberry Beryl. While Pezzottaite is closely related to the Beryl family and is visually similar, it is in fact a unique species, making its trade names somewhat misleading.

Like Emeralds, inclusions in Pezzottaite are common, especially in the larger carat weights. However, their rarity and novelty for gemstone collectors has always been the primary factor. Pezzottaite has all the attributes a gem needs - beauty, durability and rarity. Far scarcer than Ruby, these rare gems truly are a unique fashion statement.

Pezzottaite & Diamond 14K Yellow Gold Pendant

Pezzottaite & Diamond 14K Yellow Gold Ring

Pezzottaite

PEZZOTTAITE:	Initially confused with Bixbite
Origins:	Madagascar
Colors Found:	Pink to raspberry
Family:	Pezzottaite
Hardness:	7.50 - 8.00
Refractive Index:	1.60 - 1.62
Relative Density:	3.04 - 3.14

PREHNITE

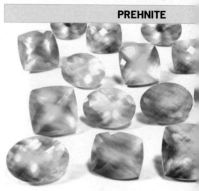

With its gorgeous greens and unique translucency, Prehnite is a wonderful rare exotic gem, which despite a suitable durability, has only recently gained popularity as a jewelry gemstone. Named after the Dutch mineralogist and early governor of the "Cape of Good Hope" colony, Colonel Hendrik Von Prehn (1733-1785), who discovered it in the Cradock district of the eastern Cape province, South Africa in the early 18th century, Prehnite was the first mineral to be named after a person.

Legend and lore

Known as the "prediction stone" among spiritual healers, it is believed that Prehnite can enhance one's dreaming and remembrance. Some crystal healers also believe that Prehnite's color and unusual touch are ideal for stress release.

Just the facts

Prehnite's bright, almost luminescent, swirling green colors (reminiscent of Jade), mesmerizing clarity and striking luster, make it an extremely attractive collector's gem. In his book, "Gemstones of the World," Walter Schumann describes Prehnite as a transparent to translucent gemstone, which accounts for its "cloudy" appearance. This is totally normal and like many gemstones, its distinctive appearance is key to its appeal. While its main colors are a range of pleasant greens that are often unique to Prehnite, yellow, gray, colorless or white varieties also exist. Prehnite has some interesting common names including "grape jade" (in China it is called "putao yu," meaning grape jade, due to crystal formations that look like a bunch of grapes), "cape emerald" (for the location of its discovery and visual similarities to Emeralds) and "prediction stone" (see above).

Prehnite & White Topaz 14K Yellow Gold Ring

Prehnite is usually found in cavities along fractures of basalt. The Australian deposits occur in scattered outcrops of Antrim Plateau Volcanics of early Cambrian age (about 570 million years old) and consist of massive basalt up to 197 feet thick. Although the primary Australian deposits cover thousands of square miles in the east Kimberley (Western Australia) and the adjoining Northern Territory, gem quality Prehnite is very scarce. With about 90% of the world's reserves of this beautiful green gem, most of the Prehnite you'll see on GemsTV hails from Australia.

Prehnite

PREHNITE:	Also known as the Prediction Stone
Origins:	Australia, China, Namibia & South Africa
Colors Found:	Colorless, green, gray, white & yellow
Family:	Silicate
Hardness:	6.00 – 6.50
Refractive Index:	1.61 – 1.67
Relative Density:	2.82 – 2.94

PYRITE (MARCASITE)

Pearl & Marcasite 925 Silver Brooch

Enamel & Marcasite 925 Silver Bracelet

PYRITE:	Called Marcasite in the jewelry trade
Origins:	Austria, China, Mexico, Romania, Russia & South Africa
Colors Found:	Golden yellow
Family:	Pyrite
Hardness:	6.00 – 6.50
Refractive Index:	None
Relative Density:	5.00 – 5.20

Pyrite has a shiny golden yellow color and a metallic luster. The name comes from the Greek word "pyr," meaning "a gemstone that strikes fire." This is due to the sparks produced when Pyrite strikes iron. While Pyrite is often mistaken for gold, they are quite different. Pyrite grains are lighter and tougher than gold, and have broken faces, properties that are not normally found in gold. Thus only a fool would mistake it for gold, which is why Pyrite is also known as "fool's gold."

Marcasite is often used as a jewelry trade name for Pyrite. Although they are called Marcasite, they are actually Pyrite, as true Marcasite is unsuitable for jewelry. The confusion between the two dates back several hundreds years due to their similar appearance. Marcasite's name was derived from "marqashith," the Arabic word for Pyrite, after an old province in northeastern Persia. Marcasite jewelry (Pyrite) is a popular style that became fashionable during Queen Victoria's reign. Marcasite jewelry normally uses Pyrite cut and polished in a circular outline (square cut gems are occasionally used) and pavé set between sterling silver beads to enhance their brilliance. They were originally used because they catch the light and glow like small diamonds. Today, Marcasite jewelry is often fashioned into 925 sterling silver rings, earrings, pendants, brooches, necklaces and bracelets.

Legends and lore

Used by the ancient Greeks in pins, earrings and amulets, Pyrite was once polished by Native Americans and used as mirrors. Pyrite is also known as "healer's gold" and is highly regarded by crystal healers as a gemstone of intellect and protection.

Just the facts

Pyrite is composed of iron sulfide. When found in its raw state, Pyrite crystals can be shaped as cubes, octahedrons and pyritohedrons (12 faces). Twinning causes "iron crosses" that look like interpenetrating cubes. Collectors particularly favor a flattened nodular variety called "Pyrite suns" or "Pyrite dollars."

Pyrite is present in igneous rocks as an accessory mineral, in sedimentary rocks, especially black shale, and in metamorphic rocks, most notably in slates. Pyrite is sometimes found as a replacement mineral in fossils.

QUARTZ

The Greeks originally named Quartz "krystallos," meaning ice, but this term was soon applied to any crystal. In fact, the modern name of Quartz is derived from the Saxon word "querklufterz," meaning "cross-vein-ore."

Although Quartz of sufficient beauty to be set into jewelry is not available in great abundance, Quartz is found in many geological environments and is a component of almost every rock type. It is also the most varied in terms of varieties, colors and forms. The gem varieties of Quartz have been used as gemstones for thousands of years.

Legends and lore

The ancients of India considered Quartz to have special properties as transformers as well as keepers of energy. To this day Quartz crystals are used universally in meditation, as they are believed to possess healing properties and other diverse metaphysical powers.

Folklorists classify Quartz as a receptive gemstone credited with the ability to attract positive energies, such as peace and love. The subtle energy of Quartz is said to balance the emotions, giving inner peace, harmony and enhancing the bonds of relationships. It is also said to calm aggression and increase self-esteem.

Champagne Quartz 14K Yellow Gold Men's Ring

Just the facts

Quartz gemstones are commonly separated into two groups based on the size of their individual crystals.

The macrocrystalline Quartz (large crystal) group includes many popular gemstones such as Amethyst, Ametrine, Citrine, Green Amethyst (Prasiolite), Rose Quartz, Rutilated Quartz, Smoky Quartz and Tiger's Eye.

Cryptocrystalline Quartz includes species whose individual crystals are too small to be easily distinguished. Apart from being a variety within the group, Chalcedony is also a catchall term to describe cryptocrystalline Quartz and includes many gems that have been coveted since antiquity such as Agate, Carnelian, Sard, Chrysoprase, Bloodstone and Jasper.

Phenomena sometimes observed in Quartz include asterism (star effect) and chatoyancy (cat's eye effect).

Rose Quartz & White Topaz 14K Yellow Gold Ring

Blue Moon Quartz

QUARTZ

Amethyst is the queen of the Quartz varieties and in better qualities it is among the most coveted of Quartzes (please see page 13 for more).

Ametrine is a multicolor variety that is part Amethyst colored and part Citrine colored (please see page 17 for more).

Blue Moon Quartz is also called Dumortierite Quartz or sometimes just Dumortierite. It is an opaque to translucent blue variety of Quartz, owing its color to microscopic inclusions of fibrous magnesioriebeckite or crocidolite. Our Blue Moon Quartz is from one of the old mines of southern Brazil in a region called Uruguaiana in the Rio Grande Do Sul state. The "Blue Moon" prefix is self-explanatory: the gem looks like a full moon shimmering on a clear night. For crystal healers, Blue Moon Quartz is a gem that can enhance organizational abilities, self discipline and orderliness.

Citrine is a yellow variety of Quartz that takes its name from "citron," the French word for lemon (please see page 30 for more).

Phantom Quartz (also known as Ghost Crystals, Specter Crystals and Shadow Crystals) is an unusual gemstone that exhibits a phenomenon called a "phantom." Phantoms can sometimes be seen in the interior of Quartz crystals as a permanent record of earlier stages in the crystal's formation, much like growth rings in a tree.

Green Amethyst (Prasiolite) is a confusing gem as it is traded under a variety of names and can easily be mistaken for other gem types (please see page 62 for more).

Rainbow Quartz (including Lavender Quartz, Neptune Quartz, Fuchsia Quartz and Coral Quartz) is visually similar to Mystic Topaz and is produced using the same physical vapor deposition (PVD) coating process. Applied to top quality natural White Quartz, the treatment is permanent with normal wear (please see page 197 for more).

Smoky Quartz is an earth toned transparent Quartz of all shades, including cognac. Also known as "champagne on ice," Smoky Quartz gets it rich warm color from aluminum. A variety of Smoky Quartz is Cairngorm, which owes its name to the legendary source in the Scottish Highlands. Smoky Quartz is the national gem of Scotland, whose national scepter includes a large Smoky Quartz on its top.

QUARTZ:	Ancient gemstone
Origins:	Brazil, Madagascar, Mozambique, South Africa & Tanzania
Colors Found:	Various
Family:	Quartz
Hardness:	7.00
Refractive Index:	1.50
Relative Density:	2.60 - 2.65

Rock Crystal (also known as White Quartz) is colorless Quartz.

Rose Quartz is the pink variety of Quartz. Rarely transparent, facet grade gems will usually display a beautiful misty appearance.

Rutile Quartz (also known as Rutilite, Rutilated Quartz, Venus' Hair or Cupid's Darts) is a beautiful gemstone produced by large inclusions of golden rutile needles in clear colorless Quartz.

Tiger's Eye is simply chatoyant Quartz (please see page 141 for more).

Star Quartz is a fascinating gem that clearly displays asterism (star effect) and is colorless, blue, pink or silver. The stars are six-rayed and roll around the gem as it is moved.

RHODOCHROSITE

Rhodochrosite (whose name means rose-colored from the Greek words "rhodon," rose and "chroma," color) is a very attractive gem with an absolutely beautiful color.

Rhodochrosite's jewelry qualities make it extremely popular. The color of a single gem can astound the observer with its vivid pink-rose hues that seem to radiate from the crystal as if lit from within.

Legends and lore

Rhodochrosite is believed by crystal healers to be a gemstone of love, balance for emotions, male and female energies, assisting in expanding consciousness and for healing mother earth.

Rhodochrosite was a popular gem during the 1930's and was often carved into decorative figurines.

Just the facts

Rhodochrosite is a manganese carbonate with colors ranging from very pale pink, pale to deep orange red, mahogany red, burnt orange, pale to dark chocolate and black. The vivid pink-rose and red colors are due to a higher manganese content. Some fine transparent crystals of Rhodochrosite are faceted into gems but this is difficult because of its perfect cleavage. As a result, Rhodochrosite is often cut and polished as cabochons, displaying bands of pink and red as well as pink and white.

Rhodochrosite 14K Yellow Gold Ring

Rhodochrosite occurs in hydrothermal mineral veins containing ores of silver, lead and copper. Individual crystals are found in rhombohedra and sometimes scalehedra, but large crystals are extremely rare.

Rhodochrosite

Rhodochrosite is found in a number of locations worldwide. For several years now the Sweet Home Mine in Alma and Sunnyside Mine in Silverton, Colorado have been mined exclusively for Rhodochrosite specimens. The Hotazel Mine in South Africa is famous for producing deep red clusters of Rhodochrosite crystals. However, the most famous mines are in the provinces of Catamarca and LaRioja, Argentina. The mines there produce an attractive pink and red banded Rhodochrosite that is colloquially called "Inca Rose."

RHODOCHROSITE:	Perfect cleavage
Origins:	Australia, Brazil, Namibia & South Africa
Colors Found:	Brown, red, pink & white
Family:	Calcite
Hardness:	3.50 - 4.50
Refractive Index:	1.60 - 1.80
Relative Density:	3.40 - 3.70

RUBY

Ruby derives its name from the Latin word for red, "rufus." The beauty, rarity and historical mystique of Rubies are undeniable. Ruby is July's birthstone, the gemstone for Capricorns and the traditional 15th and 40th anniversary gift.

Legends and lore

With the earliest record for the mining of Rubies dating to more than 2,500 years ago, the historical mystique and beauty of Rubies is as colorful as the legends and lore that surround this most precious of gems.

Prized throughout history, many believed that mystical powers lay hidden within this intensely colored red gemstone. The fiery crimson color of Rubies caused many civilizations to associate them with passion, love and romance. Rubies were also thought to bestow wisdom, health and luck in gambling.

Mentioned in Sanskrit texts, the ancient Hindus were so enchanted by the color of Rubies that they called them Ratnaraj, "the King of Gems." The ancient Hindus thought that the colors of Rubies were due to an inextinguishable fire that burned inside the gem which would endow its wearer with long life and even cause water to boil!

Royal Ruby & Diamond 14K Yellow Gold Ring

As in Sanskrit texts, biblical references to Ruby (all red gemstones were also collectively called Carbuncle at this time) refer to it as a most precious gem. In the King James Version of the Bible, Ruby (and its namesake Carbuncle) is mentioned numerous times:

Exodus 28:17

And thou shalt set in it settings of stones, even four rows of stones: the first row shall be a Sardius, a Topaz, and a Carbuncle: this shall be the first row.

Exodus 39:10

And they set in it four rows of stones: the first row was a Sardius, a Topaz, and a Carbuncle: this was the first row.

Ezekiel 28:13

Thou hast been in Eden the garden of God; every precious stone was thy covering, the Sardius, Topaz, and the Diamond, the Beryl, the Onyx, and the Jasper, the Sapphire, the Emerald, and the Carbuncle, and Gold: the workmanship of thy tabrets and of thy pipes was prepared in thee in the day that thou wast created.

Royal Ruby & White Topaz 14K Yellow Gold Ring

109

RUBY

Ruby & Diamond 14K Yellow Gold Ring

Ruby & Diamond 14K White Gold Ring

Royal Ruby & White Topaz
14K Yellow Gold Men's Ring

Isaiah 54:12

And I will make thy windows of Agates, and thy gates of Carbuncles, and all thy borders of pleasant stones.

Job 28:18

No mention shall be made of Coral, or of Pearls: for the price of wisdom is above Rubies.

Proverbs 3:15

She is more precious than Rubies: and all the things thou canst desire are not to be compared unto her.

Proverbs 8:11

For wisdom is better than Rubies; and all the things that may be desired are not to be compared to it.

Proverbs 20:15

There is gold, and a multitude of Rubies: but the lips of knowledge are a precious jewel.

Lamentations 4:7

Her Nazarites were purer than snow, they were whiter than milk, they were more ruddy in body than Rubies, their polishing was of Sapphire.

Interestingly, the gems called "Rubies" in the Old Testament may have actually been Spinel or Garnet. Up until the 18th century, when chemical testing was improved, most red gems were called Rubies. In fact, many of the famous Rubies in the crown jewels of Europe have since been identified as Spinel or Garnet. For example, the Black Prince Ruby that rests proudly at the center of the British Imperial State Crown is actually a red Spinel!

Ancient Ceylonese legends (modern day Sri Lanka) relate the story of the destruction of their demonic King Ravana. They believed that after his demise, his blood turned into Rubies resulting in their intense red color.

Native Americans believed that offerings of a fine Ruby resulted in rebirth as a powerful Chief.

Some cultures believed Ruby's blood-like color would protect the wearer from injury. In fact, ancient Burmese warriors believed that when a Ruby was inserted beneath the skin it generated a mystical force, making them unconquerable in battle.

In the 13th century, the renowned explorer Marco Polo wrote that Kublai Kahn, the Mongol Emperor of China, once offered an entire city for a Ruby the size of a man's finger.

Because of its fluorescent properties, a giant Ruby once lit an entire chamber in a palace of a Chinese emperor!

In the Middle Ages, Rubies were thought to contain prophetic powers. It was believed that a Ruby could warn its owner of misfortunes by deepening in color.

Just the facts

Like many "allochromatic" (other colored) gems whose colors are due to trace elements, apart from their color, Rubies are identical to Sapphires. Rubies and Sapphires are comprised of the mineral known as Corundum. The crystalline form of aluminum oxide, the name Corundum is believed to be derived from three ancient Tamil, Hindi and Sanskrit words for Rubies and Sapphires, "kurundam," "kurund" or "kuruvinda" respectively.

Did you know that Rubies are rarer than Diamonds? In the last 60 years hardly a month has passed without a new Diamond deposit being discovered. In contrast, Rubies are only found in a handful of mines worldwide.

Did you know that Rubies are more expensive than Diamonds? A 16 carat Ruby that sold at Sotheby's in New York in October 1988 fetched a staggering $3,630,000!

Second only to Diamonds in hardness, Rubies are one of the toughest gemstones and with no cleavage, breakage rarely occurs. This combined with the fact that Rubies come in many different shapes and sizes, makes them perfect for all types of jewelry.

While color preferences are subjective, the best Rubies possess an intense, almost electric red effect due to fluorescence. Color is the most important factor when evaluating Rubies. While cutting and size (fine Rubies over 2 carats are very scarce) is also important, transparency is secondary. Why is this? Colored by chromium and other trace elements, Rubies formed millions of years ago deep within the earth. As very few Rubies crystallized undisturbed, a whole host of tiny irregularities (inclusions) are a characteristic of their formation. Far from being flaws, inclusions are a fascinating hallmark of authenticity that records a gem's natural relationship with the Earth.

Microscopic rutile inclusions, commonly known as "silk," are a normal characteristic of Rubies. When

Ruby, White Sapphire & Diamond 14K Yellow Gold Pendant

Ruby 14K Yellow Gold Ring

Vietnamese Star Ruby

RUBY

Ruby & Diamond 14K Yellow Gold Ring

Majestic Ruby & Diamond 18K Yellow Gold Ring

evenly distributed, small quantities of "silk" enhance a Ruby's beauty by creating a soft uniform distribution of light or sparkle.

Asterism or the "star effect" is a reflection effect that appears as two or more intersecting bands of light across the surface of a gem. This rare phenomenon is found in both Rubies and Sapphires.

As Rubies come in many different colors and sizes, ultimately your personal preference should be your primary concern. But what is the difference between a Royal and Majestic Ruby? At GemsTV, "Royal" relates to size (2 carats or more) while "Majestic" is our own term used to describe superior quality (color and clarity) in gemstones. In our opinion, Majestic Ruby is some of the best Ruby available.

Our Madagascan Rubies are mined at high altitude, deep within an impenetrable jungle. The only way to reach the Ruby mines near the mining village of Moramanga is by helicopter or a grueling long day's trek (11 hours) on a muddy trail through dense mountainous rainforest from the Madagascan town of Andilamena. A relatively new deposit found in July 2004 yields our Majestic Ruby. However, since mid-2006 these deposits have reportedly been nearing depletion. This increasing scarcity makes these Rubies a must for any jewelry collection.

Apart from Madagascar, we also source Rubies from Vietnam, Tanzania, Kenya, Sri Lanka, China, and of course, Thailand. However, strict environmental regulations combined with depletion have resulted in the reduction of Thai gem mining.

With approximately 70% of the world's Sapphire output and 90% of its Ruby production passing though Thailand (Source: ICA 2006 World Colored Gemstone Mining Report), our craftspeople are the first to choose the finest examples. We use Rubies when handcrafting all manner of gorgeous jewelry and being the gem of love and passion, Rubies are hard to resist.

RUBY:	July's birthstone
Origins:	India, Kenya, Madagascar, Sri Lanka, Tanzania, Thailand & Vietnam
Colors Found:	Red
Family:	Corundum
Hardness:	9.00
Refractive Index:	1.76 - 1.77
Relative Density:	3.90 - 4.10

Majestic Ruby

*"They brought me Rubies from the mine, and held them to the
sun; I said, 'they are drops of frozen wine
from Eden's vats that run'."*

Ralph Waldo Emerson

SAPPHIRE

Blue Sapphire & Diamond 14K White Gold Ring

Blue Sapphire 14K Yellow Gold Ring

Ceylon Sapphire

Sapphires derive their name from the Latin word "sapphirus," meaning blue, and are often referred to as the "gem of the heavens" or the "celestial gem," as their colors mirror the sky at different times of the day.

The word Sapphire, stated without a prefix, implies Blue Sapphires only. Sapphires of all other colors are assigned a color prefix or are collectively termed "Fancy Sapphires."

Legends and lore

Blue is one of the favorite colors of both men and women and is a color psychologically linked to the emotions of sympathy, calmness and loyalty.

Legend has it that the first person to wear Sapphire was Prometheus, the rival of Zeus, who took the gemstone from Cacaus, where he also stole fire from heaven for man.

The ancient Persians believed Sapphires were a chip from the pedestal that supported the earth, and that its reflections gave the sky its colors.

Sapphire is mentioned in the Bible as being one of the twelve "stones of fire" (Ezekiel 28:13-16) that were given to Moses and set in the breastplate of Aaron (Exodus 28:15-30). Sapphire is also one of the twelve gemstones set in the foundations of the city walls of Jerusalem (Revelations 21:19) and associated with the Apostle St. Paul.

The guardians of innocence, Sapphires symbolize truth, sincerity and faithfulness, and are thought to bring peace, joy and wisdom to their owners. In ancient times it was believed that when the wearer of a Sapphire faced challenging obstacles, the gem's power enabled them to find the correct solution.

In India it was believed that a Sapphire immersed in water formed an elixir that could cure the bite of scorpions and snakes. Alternatively, if it were worn as a talisman pendant, it would protect the wearer against evil spirits.

The following legend is Burmese in origin and highlights Sapphires' connection with faithfulness: "Eons ago Tsun-Kyan-Kse, a golden haired goddess with Sapphire blue eyes, presided lovingly over the temple of Lao-Tsun. Everyday, the temple's chief monk Mun-Ha, meditated before the golden goddess accompanied by his devoted companion, a green-eyed cat named Sinh. One day the temple was besieged by

SAPPHIRE

a group of terrible outlaws. When they threw Mun-Ha to the floor, Sinh leapt fiercely at the bandits, jumping up on his master's chest to protect him. The wrong doers fled screaming in fear, never to return and in gratitude for his courage, the golden goddess awarded Sinh with her Sapphire blue eyes. To this day, Sinh's ancestors guard over the temple." The temple still stands and is populated by Siamese cats with striking blue eyes (typically this breed has green eyes).

For hundreds of years Blue Sapphires were the popular choice for engagement and wedding rings.

In many cultures Star Sapphires were considered love charms; Helen of Troy was said to have owned a Star Sapphire and to have owed her conquests to it! In 17th century Germany, Star Sapphires were the "siegstein," meaning "victory stone." To others, Star Sapphires were the "stone of destiny," as their crossing bands of light were believed to represent faith, hope and destiny. Star Sapphires were commonly used as talismans to protect against the evil eye and the Sinhalese used them to guard against witchcraft. The famous English traveler, Sir Richard Francis Burton, possessed a large specimen which he referred to as his talisman, claiming it brought him good horses and prompt attention wherever he went. In fact, it was only in those places where he received proper attention that he would show it, a favor greatly appreciated because the sight of the gem was believed to bring good luck. The fame of Burton's Star Sapphire traveled ahead of him, serving him as a guiding star. One of the most unique of all talismanic gems, Star Sapphires are said to be so potent that they continue to exercise their good influence over the first wearer even if it has passed into other hands.

Ceylon Sapphire 18K White Gold Ring

Just the facts

The modern popularity of Padparadscha and Pink Sapphires aside, Blue Sapphires are traditionally the most coveted members of the Sapphire family. Coming in a wide variety of hues, Sapphires range in color from pastel blues all the way through to the depths of midnight blue. Sapphires are identical to Ruby (the red variety of Corundum), except for one key component, their color. Sapphires are "allochromatic" (other colored) gems and obtain their colors due to the presence of trace elements including iron and titanium. The crystalline form of aluminum oxide, the name Corundum is believed to

Ceylon Sapphire & White Sapphire 18K Yellow Gold Ring

Ceylon Sapphire 14K Yellow Gold Ring

SAPPHIRE

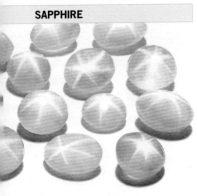

Ceylon Sapphire 18K Yellow Gold Ring

Blue Sapphire 14K White Gold Ring

Ceylon Sapphire & Diamond 14K Yellow Gold Ring

be derived from three ancient Tamil, Hindi and Sanskrit words for Rubies and Sapphires, "kurundam," "kurund" or "kuruvinda" respectively.

While personal preference should always be your primary concern when purchasing colored gemstones, Sapphires that sit in the middle of the blue color range are historically the most coveted.

Sapphires are one of the toughest gemstones, second in hardness only to Diamonds. Corundum is primarily mined from alluvial deposits and only occasionally from host rock deposits just beneath the earth's surface.

Asterism or the "star effect" is a reflection effect that appears as two or more intersecting bands of light across the surface of a gem. This rare phenomenon is found in both Sapphires and Rubies.

Sapphire locations and varieties

As Sapphires from different locations can vary slightly in appearance, we have detailed some of our main sources and varieties below.

Australian Sapphire

Some of the finest Sapphires in the world herald from this sun-burnt country. Top quality Australian Sapphires exhibit brilliant cornflower blues usually associated with those from Ceylon (Sri Lanka). Sapphires have been mined in Australia for over 100 years. The majority of Australian Sapphires come from three fields: the Anakie fields in central Queensland, the Lava Plains in northern Queensland and the New England fields around Inverell in the northeast of New South Wales.

During the 1980's Australia produced approximately 70% of the world's Sapphires and although production has decreased, the demand from the international market for Australian Sapphires remains very high. Sapphires found in Australia originate from similar geological conditions to those of Thailand and Cambodia, and thus possess similar characteristics.

Ceylon Sapphire (Sri Lanka)

The island of Ceylon (known as Sri Lanka since 1972) holds the earliest records for the mining of Sapphires. Noted for their royal and cornflower blues, Ceylon Sapphires are synonymous with top quality Sapphires

SAPPHIRE

and are highly coveted. A classic source of quality Sapphires throughout history (King Solomon reportedly wooed the Queen of Sheba with Sri Lankan Sapphires), mining occurs in the gem rich alluvial gravels found beneath the tea-covered slopes of Elahera and Rathnapura (which literally means "gem city").

Ceylon Sapphires received a boost in their popularity in 1981 when Prince Charles gave Lady Diana an engagement ring set with a stunning 18 carat Ceylon Sapphire.

At GemsTV, we use the prefix "Ceylon" to denote a quality as well as an origin (not all Sri Lankan Sapphires can be called "Ceylon").

Kanchanaburi Sapphire (Thailand)

The sleepy province of Kanchanaburi, renowned for the bridge over the River Kwai, rests among the jungle clad valleys of western Thailand. Kanchanaburi's Bo Ploi Sapphire mines were discovered in 1918 and today remain one of world's premier sources of Blue Sapphires. The Sapphires of Bo Ploi are mined from alluvial deposits spread over 1.2 square miles. The miners of Bo Ploi must unearth over 50 tons of alluvial soil to extract just 1 carat of Sapphire crystal. Sapphires have been heavily mined from the Bo Ploi mines in the last ten years and are approaching depletion. This increasing rarity makes these Sapphires a must for any jewelry collection.

Blue Sapphire 18K White Gold Ring

Madagascan Sapphire

Today, Madagascar also provides some of the highest quality Sapphires. Sapphires were first unearthed on this island in the early 1990's. The Madagascan gem fields now reportedly account for approximately 20% of the world's Sapphires. The majority of Madagascar's Sapphires come from the prolific gem fields of Ilakaka, Antiermene and Diego Suarez.

Ceylon Sapphire & Diamond 18K Yellow Gold Pendant

Midnight Blue Sapphire

Midnight Blue Sapphire combines deep rich colors and a spellbinding luster all in one gemstone. Deep blues intermingle in Midnight Blue Sapphire as if to reveal the secret of the sky at night. This accentuates their luster and is one reason for their enduring popularity. Mined in a wide variety of countries including Madagascar, Australia, Nigeria, Thailand,

Midnight Blue Sapphire 14K White Gold Ring

SAPPHIRE

Vietnam and China, Midnight Blue Sapphire is a gemstone whose colors are beyond vivid. But there is nothing black about Midnight Blue Sapphire. To visualize this, think of the color of a desert sky shortly after the sun has set, with stars rising in the distance. This is the color of Midnight Blue Sapphire, an intense azure hue unmatched in the gem kingdom.

Nigerian Sapphire

Nigeria plays a key role in supplying the world with some of the most popular gemstones. Nigerian Sapphire is mined at Nisama Jama'a in Nigeria's Kaduna State.

Pailin Sapphire (Cambodia)

Ceylon Sapphire 14K Yellow Gold Ring

The Cambodian city of Pailin (the ancient Khmer word for "Blue Sapphire") is steeped in local folklore regarding its precious treasures: "Long ago, people hunting in the forests around Pailin encountered a magical old lady called Yiey Yat ("yiey" means grandmother in Khmer) living as a hermit in the mountains. Fearing for the local wildlife, she told the villagers that if they stopped hunting, the gods would reward them with something of far greater value in the streams and rivers of Mount Yat. The people went there and saw an otter ("pey" in Khmer) playing ("leng" in Khmer) in a stream. Swimming up to them, when the otter opened its mouth, it was full of gems!" As a result, the area and its Sapphires are known as "pey leng," which when translated to Thai became Pailin. Even today, many people visit the shrine of Yiey Yat to ask her for riches.

SAPPHIRE

Royal Sapphire

As larger Sapphires dramatically increase in scarcity, regardless of locale, we clearly identify these for you in our product descriptions. At GemsTV, "Royal" denotes Sapphires 2 carats and over.

Shangdong Sapphire (China)

While China has never been considered an historical source of Corundum (domestic finds were not reported until the late 1970's), the Chinese were aware of and coveted Ruby and Sapphire from other locales as early as 319 AD. Chinese Sapphire deposits are widely distributed over 20 of the country's provinces, although they are mainly found along the eastern coastline. In all of these places, Sapphires occur in basalts, similar to those mined in Australia. Among these localities, the deposit in Shangdong province has the best quality. Shangdong Sapphire was discovered near Wutu, Changle County, Shangdong province in the late 1980's, initially in alluvial deposits and later in the host basalt. Gem mining occurs in the secondary alluvial deposits while the primary deposits are worked for mineral specimens. Generally, Chinese Blue Sapphires have a deep blue color, but similar to Sapphires from Ban Kha Ja, Chanthaburi and Australia, greenish blues and yellows are also found. Chinese Sapphires are a lot more than dark inky gems that appear more black than blue. While Shangdong Sapphire has royal blues that are beyond vivid, it also has a transparency far greater than most Midnight Blue Sapphire. In the Shangdong province there are reportedly at least 20 small Sapphire mines operated by 200-300 miners.

Shangdong Sapphire & White Topaz 14K Yellow Gold Ring

Umba River Sapphire (Tanzania)

On the Great North Road in Tanzania, between the plains of the Serengeti and the foothills of Mount Kilimanjaro lies Arusha, the gateway to the beating heart of Africa and home to the fabled gemstone mines of the Umba Valley. Collecting in rich alluvial deposits that run the course of the valley, Umba River Sapphire is sourced using age-old mining techniques by Waarusha and Wameru miners whose knowledge of gemstones has been handed down for generations.

Color Change Sapphire 14K Yellow Gold Earrings

SAPPHIRE (FANCY)

Chanthaburi Black Star Sapphire

Sri Lankan Color Change Sapphire in different lighting conditions

Since the dawn of time, Sapphires have captivated and mesmerized jewelry connoisseurs the world over. From hot pink to forest green, Sapphire's spectrum of colors is truly kaleidoscopic.

Fancy Sapphires get their unique colors from the iron, chromium, titanium and other trace metals present within the Corundum.

Chanthaburi Sapphire (Thailand)

Black Star Sapphires have only ever been found at one place on Earth – Ban Kha Ja, Chanthaburi (located approximately 152 miles east of Bangkok, close to the border of Cambodia). From these mines, no more than 4 miles from the GemsTV workshops, stunning blue, green and yellow Sapphires are also unearthed. Displaying gorgeous golden tangerine hues, a stunning Sapphire variety we aptly called "Chanthaburi Sapphire" from a new alluvial pocket at Ban Kha Ja proved hugely popular in 2005.

Black Star Sapphires differ from other Corundum in that their color is not due to trace elements or color centers. It is instead caused by the color of exsolved hematite-ilmenite silk inclusions. This silk imparts a deep brown black color to an otherwise blue, green or yellow Sapphire. This is called "mechanical coloration" or "color by inclusions." Not only are they responsible for color, but they also produce a six-rayed star effect. When it occurs in an otherwise blue or green Sapphire, the rays of the star appear white. Sometimes the hematite unmixes in a yellow Sapphire, giving the star a golden yellow color.

Today, mining in Chanthaburi is very limited making top quality Sapphires from this town exceedingly rare. In fact, we think what is being traded in the local market is older stock, with very few new gems being unearthed.

Color Change Sapphire

While Color Change Sapphires come from a variety of locations, the gem gravels of Tanzania are the main source. Color Change Sapphires present gem lovers with an opportunity to own the rare and stunning color change effect in a gem other than Alexandrite or Garnet. While the colors tend to vary a bit depending on locale, in general they change from khaki green to reddish purple. The picture of a notable exception from Sri Lanka, changing from purple to red, is included on the previous page.

Green Sapphire

Green Sapphires display a range of green hues, from tropical limes to wine bottle greens.

Padparadscha & Padparadscha Color Sapphire

While Sapphires have mesmerized jewelry connoisseurs since the dawn of time, there is one Sapphire variety that mesmerizes above all others, the mysterious and coveted Padparadscha Sapphire.

Padparadscha Sapphire derives its name from its resemblance to the beautiful and famed pinkish orange red lotus flower known to the Sri Lankan people as "Padparadscha" or in botanical terms Nelumbo Nucifera Speciosa.

Padparadscha Sapphires must combine elements of pink and orange in one gem to rightly claim their Padparadscha title. One way to picture the color of Padparadscha Sapphires is to imagine sitting in front of a lazy fire on an isolated beach painted by the soothing hues of a tropical sunset. You then hold a fragrant lotus bloom to your nose and at that instant, the colors meld creating an aurora of orange and pink. This is Padparadscha!

Wonderfully romantic and delightfully seductive, Padparadscha Sapphires are so rare and beautiful that they are highly prized by collectors. But what are the origins of the word Padparadscha?

Often misunderstood, with no universal agreement as to its meaning, the modern word "Padparadscha" was in fact adopted from a German gemological text early in the 20th century. The word Padparadscha is actually a corruption of two Sanskrit and Singhalese words "padma raga." While "padma" means lotus, the word "raga" is more complex, meaning color, attraction, desire and musical rhythm all in rolled into one! Interestingly, the original term had much broader applications and was even used in ancient times to describe a variety of Ruby. A medieval Prakit text on gemology called the "Thakkura Pheru's Rayanaparikkha," describes Padparadscha Sapphires as "that which spreads its rays like the sun, is glossy, soft to the touch, resembling the fire, like molten gold and not worn off is Padma Raga."

SAPPHIRE (FANCY)

Ceylon Padparadscha Color Sapphire 18K Yellow Gold Ring

Ceylon Padparadscha Color Sapphire 18K Yellow Gold Ring

Ceylon Padparadscha Color Sapphire

SAPPHIRE (FANCY)

Identical in appearance to Padparadscha Sapphires, Padparadscha Color Sapphires are created through recent innovations in heat treatment developed in Chanthaburi, Thailand, the location of the GemsTV jewelry workshops. To learn more about this treatment please see page 197 of this guide.

Although the exact description is often debated, the beauty of these rare gemstones is not. While some continue to narrowly define Padparadscha as a Sri Lankan Sapphire, today Padparadscha and Padparadscha Color Sapphires are recognized as also hailing from Madagascar, Vietnam and Tanzania. Regardless of the locale, Padparadscha Sapphires and Padparadscha Color Sapphires, especially in larger sizes, are incredibly scarce.

Don't forget that like many of the rarer gemstones we offer, there is never a guarantee of continuous supply. Padparadscha Sapphire and Padparadscha Color Sapphire certainly fits into this category and it can take months of hard work to accumulate enough even for a few jewelry lines.

Pink Sapphire

Immensely popular, Pink Sapphires range from pastel to vivacious pinks and share a color border with Ruby. While some Pink Sapphires are so close to this boundary they are called "Hot Pink," at GemsTV we use our own term "Majestic" to differentiate this color variety. Sharing exactly the same position on the color wheel, red and pink are technically the same color. It is the saturation or strength of this red hue that differentiates red from pink. The problem is that the border region where pink stops and red starts is open to interpretation. To put the issue to rest, the International Colored Gemstone Association (ICA) stated the following: "Pink is really just light red. The International Colored Gemstone Association has passed a resolution that the light shades of the red hue should be included in the Ruby category since it was too difficult to legislate where red ended and pink began. In practice, pink shades are now known either as Pink Ruby or Pink Sapphire."

Purple Sapphire

Prized by collectors, Purple Sapphires (also once known as Oriental Amethyst) can display rich purple-pink colors reminiscent of orchids. One word of warning: when we manage to source Purple

Majestic Pink Sapphire & Diamond 18K White Gold Ring

Purple Sapphire & Diamond 18K White Gold Ring

Yellow Sapphire 14K Yellow Gold Ring

Sapphires, they don't stay in our vaults for very long as they are quickly snapped up by collectors and jewelry connoisseurs alike.

Yellow Sapphire

Ranging from pleasing pastel daisies to intensely beautiful canary yellows, Yellow Sapphires are renowned for their amazing luster and brilliance. Yellow Sapphires are not just beautiful, but are also one of the most coveted of all yellow gemstones.

Star Sapphire

With their very bright and lustrous star formations, Star Sapphires have traditionally been the most popular of all star gemstones. Glance at a Star Sapphire and you will see six or even twelve rayed stars silently gliding across the gemstone's surface. This wonderful gem has long been coveted for its beautiful and mysterious optical effect known as "asterism." "Asterism" or the "asteric effect" is caused by sets of parallel needle-like inclusions within the gemstone. While the gem gravels of Rathnapura in Sri Lanka are one of the world's main sources of Star Sapphires, Black Star Sapphires are only found in the Ban Kha Ja district in Chanthaburi province of Thailand.

Sunset Sapphire

While it might not have the pinks to be Padparadscha, there is nothing about the beauty of Sunset Sapphires that is lacking. Displaying a bright blend of crimson tangerines reminiscent of an African sunset, Sunset Sapphire (also called Songea Sapphire) was only discovered in 1992. The world's only Sunset Sapphire deposit is located 37 miles west of Songea, with the Masuguru district being the main mining area. Discoveries like Sunset Sapphire have helped Songea become the second most important Tanzanian mining area after Merelani (the home of Tanzanite).

White Sapphire

The ancient Egyptians associated White Sapphire with the all-seeing eye of Horus, while the Greeks linked it to their god Apollo, using it in the prophesizing of the oracles at Delphi.

SAPPHIRE (FANCY)

White Sapphire 14K Yellow Gold Ring

Sunset Sapphire

SAPPHIRE:	September's birthstone
Origins:	Australia, Cambodia, China, Kenya, Madagascar, Nigeria, Sri Lanka, Tanzania, Thailand & Vietnam
Colors Found:	Various
Family:	Corundum
Hardness:	9.00
Refractive Index:	1.76 - 1.77
Relative Density:	3.90 - 4.10

123

SAPPHIRE (FANCY)

The ancient Greeks unearthed White Sapphires from the island of Naxos in the Aegean Sea.

With none of the iron, chromium, titanium and other trace metals that give Fancy Sapphires their unique colors, White Sapphire is arguably Sapphire in its purest form. Displaying an exceptional luster and brilliance, it has become a popular alternative to Diamonds.

SCAPOLITE

Coming in colorless, pink, purple, blue, yellow and silver hues, Scapolite was discovered in 1913 in the Mogok stone tract of upper Myanmar (Burma). Scapolite comes from the Greek words "scapos," meaning rod and "lithos," meaning stone. It gets its name from the stick or rod-like appearance of its crystals. Scapolite is also known as Wernerite for the German explorer and mineralogist Abraham Gottlob Werner (1750–1817).

Legends and lore

While Scapolite has no specific legends and lore, its Cat's Eye variety has been attributed with some metaphysical attributes. Wearing a Cat's Eye is believed by some to make one wealthy, healthy, strongly determined and knowledgeable as well as providing protection from enemies. It is also believed to help one gain insight and psychic powers.

Just the facts

As Scapolite is a mixture of minerals, with varying specific gravity and refractive indexes, it can easily be confused with Amethyst, Citrine, Chrysoberyl and Golden Beryl. However, Scapolite can be differentiated from these other gems by the use of a long-wave ultraviolet (UV) light. Scapolite fluoresces with a yellowish to orange color, while Quartz and Beryl do not display such fluorescence.

Scapolite & White Topaz 14K Yellow Gold Ring

Scapolite minerals are silicates of aluminum with calcium and sodium. Scapolite is usually found as prismatic crystals in metamorphic rocks and only very occasionally in igneous rocks.

While facet grade Scapolite can be transparent with a fine color, less transparent crystals are often polished as cabochons to exhibit exquisite Cat's Eyes.

Although very attractive, Scapolite is not a well known gemstone, mainly due to its extreme scarcity. Definitely one for collectors, this gem makes only a few rare appearances on GemsTV.

Scapolite & White Topaz 14K White Gold Ring

Scapolite

SCAPOLITE:	Mixture of minerals
Origins:	Brazil, China, India, Madagascar, Mozambique, Sri Lanka & Tanzania
Colors Found:	Yellowish to orange
Family:	Scapolite
Hardness:	5.50 - 6.00
Refractive Index:	1.54 - 6.00
Relative Density:	2.56 - 2.77

SILLIMANITE

Star Sillimanite 14K Yellow Gold Ring

Star Sillimanite 14K Yellow Gold Men's Ring

Beautiful and rare, Sillimanite is named for the famous American geologist Benjamin Silliman (1779-1864). Sillimanite is sometime referred to as Fibrolite. Sillimanite is not only scarce, but also difficult for miners to identify and problematic for cutters. These three attributes combine to ensure that Sillimanite remains a true exotic gemstone.

Just the facts

Sillimanite is formed from aluminum silicate and is usually found as silky, fibrous crystals suitable for cabochons. Transparent crystals suitable for faceting display a glassy luster and are exceedingly scarce. Sillimanite is colorless, white, brown, yellow, blue and green in color.

Sillimanite is typically found scattered within layers of metamorphic rocks that have been put under great pressure and high temperature. This is why Sillimanite is commonly found in volcanic or hot spring areas. Because of the way it is scattered within the host rocks, miners often have difficulty in detecting Sillimanite.

Sillimanite is a polymorph with two other minerals, Kyanite and Andalusite. A polymorph is a mineral that shares the same chemistry but a different crystal structure with another, or other, minerals. This is unusual, and due to its brittleness, Sillimanite is very difficult to facet. Some 50% of gem quality crystals can be damaged during the faceting and fashioning process alone!

Some Sillimanite crystals demonstrate chatoyancy (also known as the "cat's eye effect," caused by minerals reflecting a single band of light back to the eye), and make stunning cabochon rings and earrings.

SILLIMANITE:	Polymorph
Origins:	Brazil, India & Sri Lanka
Colors Found:	Blue, brown, colorless, green, white & yellow
Family:	Sillimanite
Hardness:	6.00 - 7.00
Refractive Index:	1.65 - 1.68
Relative Density:	3.24

Sillimanite

SPHENE

Sphene is named after the Greek word for wedge, because its crystals are typically wedge shaped. As it contains titanium, Sphene is also sometimes referred to by its mineral name, Titanite.

One of the world's newest and rarest gems, Sphene possesses the rather unusual ability to take a beam of light and break it into all of the spectral colors, a feature gemologically referred to as fire or dispersion. In this regard Sphene is superior to Diamond. This combined with its strong pleochroism (different colors are displayed when the gemstone is viewed from different angles) has the effect of making the gem appear to change color. Occasionally pink, black or chocolate, most Sphene is predominantly green or yellowish-green, with just about every other color of the rainbow displayed by its intense fiery brilliance.

Just the facts

Sphene makes gorgeously brilliant, fiery gems that have a higher dispersion (fire) than Diamonds.

Sphene's magnificent fire, unique color shades, strong pleochroism, adamantine (Diamond-like) luster and double refraction (birefringence) make it ideal for earrings and pendants that catch the light, displaying its sparkling qualities to full effect. A unique characteristic of Sphene is birefringence (doubly refractive), meaning that light splits into two rays as it passes through the gem. As a result, the back facets appear as double images giving it a beautiful soft hazy appearance similar to the doubling seen in Zircon.

Sphene & White Topaz 14K Yellow Gold Ring

If well polished the luster can approach or equal that of Diamond, but Sphene is notoriously difficult to polish well. A well polished Sphene is testament to an experienced jeweler. The cutters at GemsTV always take great care to ensure that our Sphene is finished in a manner that maximizes its intense natural beauty.

Sphene larger than a few carats without inclusions is extremely scarce.

Sphene & White Topaz 14K White Gold Ring

Sphene

SPHENE:	Fire greater than Diamond
Origins:	Brazil, Madagascar, Pakistan & Sri Lanka
Colors Found:	Yellowish-green
Family:	Sphene
Hardness:	5.50
Refractive Index:	1.885 - 2.05
Relative Density:	3.40 - 3.56

127

SPINEL

Noble Red Spinel & White Topaz 14K White Gold Ring

Noble Red Spinel 14K Yellow Gold Ring

Noble Red Spinel & White Topaz 14K Yellow Gold Ring

Spinel was once mistaken for Ruby and Sapphire, but it's no impostor, rather a "master of disguise." One of the gem kingdom's best kept secrets, Spinel is treasured for its eternal brilliance and spectacular colors. Whether your fascination with gems is for their beauty, rarity or history, Spinel is a superb addition to your jewelry collection.

Spinel's name is derived either from the Latin word for thorn "spina," as a result of its characteristic octahedral crystals having pointed ends, or from the Greek word for spark "spintharis," in reference to the gem's bright red hues.

Legends and lore

Due to its mistaken identity, Spinel has few historical references. However, Spinels have a bizarre association with sorcerers and alchemists. Spinels were used by practitioners of the "dark arts" to summon demons and also used as amulets to protect them from fire. One tale describes how Spinels could be used to work against their masters. Those thought to possess supernatural powers were found guilty if they began to shake when approached with a Spinel wrapped in paper!

Spinels occupy a unique place in gemstone history. Despite being recognized as a separate gem species in 1587, up until the 19th century the intense coloration displayed by Noble Red Spinel led some to mistakenly identify this gem as Ruby. The source of confusion stemmed not only from color similarities but also the close proximity of their deposits. It was not until 1783 that Rome de Lisle became the first scientist to clearly distinguish differences between Ruby and Noble Red Spinel.

Noble Red Spinel's near identical resemblance to Ruby results in it being a prodigious, albeit accidental feature in many of the world's most famous gem collections, including the Vatican's and the Crown Jewels of Russia, Iran and England. Interestingly, both the legendary 352 carat "Timur Ruby" and the 170 carat "Black Prince's Ruby," which feature in the British Imperial State Crown proved to be Noble Red Spinel!

In 1415 at the Battle of Agincourt the English King, Henry V wore a helmet garnished with jewels including the "Black Prince's Ruby." During the battle, the French commander, the Duke of Alencon, struck Henry's head a mighty blow with his battle-axe, nearly killing the King. Surprisingly, the force of the blow glanced off the Spinel saving his life and allowed Henry to lead his troops to what many thought would be an impossible victory.

Just the facts

Spinel occurs in many colors including red, blue, pink, orange and a plethora of other fancy colors. Apart from color prefixes, some of Spinel's other names include:

Almandine Spinel	The violet variety of Spinel.
Balas Ruby	This is an historical name for Spinel, which referred to the country of origin; either Badakshan in Tajikistan or the Balaksh region of Sri Lanka.
Cobalt Blue Spinel	Resembling fine Sapphires, these exceptional Blue Spinels from Sri Lanka and Tanzania are colored by Cobalt. Regular Blue Spinel also hails from Tanzania and displays similar visual similarities to Sapphire, particularly those from Montana.
Flame Spinel	The orange red variety of Spinel.
Gahnite or Gahnospinel	Named after Swedish chemist L. G. Gahn, it is the rare greenish or bluish, zinc-rich variety of Spinel.
Noble Red Spinel	The Ruby red variety of Spinel was historically mistaken for Ruby.
Rubicelle	The yellow to orange variety of Spinel.

Fancy Spinel 14K Yellow Gold Ring

Purple Spinel 14K Yellow Gold Ring

The reality behind Noble Red Spinel's Ruby-like appearance is its proximity to Corundum deposits, the base mineral of Rubies and Sapphires, and chromium, the midas element responsible for giving both Noble Red Spinels and Rubies their deep red color.

Today, Spinels can be easily identified by their refractivity. Since Noble Red Spinels are singly refractive and Rubies doubly refractive, the primary color in Noble Red Spinels appears purer and more intense than the reds seen in many Rubies.

Spinels are mined from alluvial deposits or directly from large granular granite or other igneous host rocks. Spinels come from a handful of sources

Cobalt Blue Spinel & White Topaz 14K White Gold Ring

SPINEL

including Madagascar, Tunduru in Tanzania's remote southeast and central Vietnam's Luc Yen region. While most gemstone aficionados know Burma (now Myanmar) to be the classic and most familiar source for fine Noble Red Spinel, new discoveries in Tanzania's Kilimanjaro region are shifting paradigms. Tanzanian Noble Red Spinel is increasingly acclaimed for its bright red hues and a brilliance and luster that defy verbal description.

Perfect octahedral crystals are sometimes set into jewelry in their original uncut octahedral shapes. The Burmese refer to these gems as "nat thwe," meaning spirit polished. Sometimes "nat thwe" Spinels will receive a very light polishing.

Pure Spinel is white, but impurities give it a wide range of colors. Almost all colors are used in jewelry, but the most valuable and popular color is Noble Red Spinel. Occasionally, color change varieties are found, turning color from a light gray blue in daylight to a light purple under candlelight.

Noble Red Spinel & White Topaz 14K Yellow Gold Ring

Even though they are more affordable, did you know that Spinels are rarer than Rubies? In the gem kingdom, "rare" can be both a blessing and a curse, as this affects market prices and availability. This is unfortunate for the Spinel miner, but great news for everyone else as they are one of nature's most beautiful treasures.

Spinels are intensely colored durable gemstones perfect for all jewelry. Spinel's high refractive index makes cutting very important, as the quality of the cut will affect its brilliance. Naturally, all Spinels sold at GemsTV are faceted by experienced cutters who always take each gemstone's physical properties and individual attributes into consideration.

Noble Red Spinel 14K Yellow Gold Ring

Noble Red Spinel

SPINEL:	Once confused with Ruby and Sapphire
Origins:	Madagascar, Tanzania & Vietnam
Colors Found:	Various
Family:	Spinel
Hardness:	8.00
Refractive Index:	1.715 - 1.720
Relative Density:	3.60

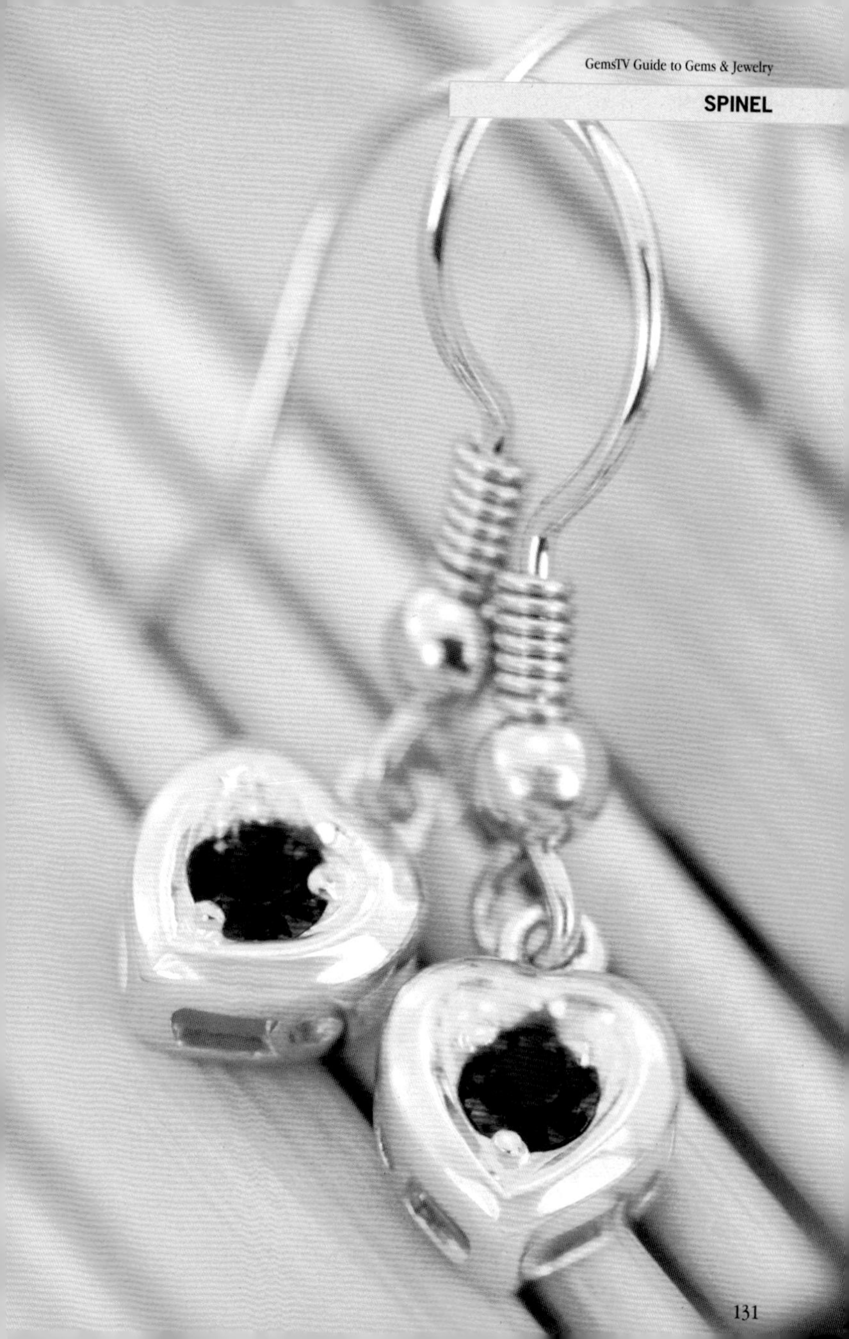

SUNSTONE

Radiating with the power of eternal light, Sunstone has been coveted since antiquity for its ability to guide its wearer through the journey of life. Sunstone is also known as Aventurine Feldspar or Heliolite, from the Greek "helios" for sun and "lithos" for stone.

Legends and lore

An ancient gem, Sunstone has allegedly been discovered in Viking burial mounds. Among the Vikings, Sunstone was thought to aid navigation both in reality and during one's journey to Valhalla and the afterlife. Interestingly, the Sunstone referenced in Norse literature probably refers to Iolite (see page 66) rather than the modern gem we call Sunstone.

Pope Clement VII (1478 - 1534) was reputed to have in his possession a Sunstone with a golden spot that moved across the surface in accordance with the apparent motion of the sun from sunrise to sunset.

Andesine 14K Yellow Gold Ring

Native Americans in Oregon used Sunstone for trade and barter. Oregon Sunstone was declared the official gemstone of the State of Oregon in 1987. Sunstone is claimed by some sources to have been used by Tibetans in medicine rituals to help spirit guides access the healing power of the Sun. When contact with the spirit guides was successful, the gem was said to glow a bright gold.

Crystal healers believe Sunstone to be useful for adding personal insight and alleviating depression. Historically, Sunstone has been linked with benevolent gods, luck and good fortune.

Just the facts

Sunstone is a member of the plagioclase Feldspar group of minerals and is closely related to Moonstone and Labradorite. The name Feldspar comes from the German "feldt spat," meaning "field stone." So named, this is because when Feldspar weathers, it releases large amounts of plant nutrients, such as potassium, which enrich soil.

Sunstone has a beautiful glittering sunlight effect as a result of its tiny metallic inclusions. The copper or pyrite inclusions cause sparkling flashes of light as millions of particles playfully interact with light. While known to gemologists as "schiller" or "aventurescence," African miners call this feature "flowers." Sunstones are nearly always cut as cabochons to reflect this phenomenon, but the

Andesine & White Topaz 14K White Gold Ring

deeper colors may also be faceted to exhibit their superior luster.

SUNSTONE

Sunstone is formed and crystallized in lava flows. Sunstones range in color from water clear through pale yellow, soft pink and red to deep blue and green. Some of the deeper colored gems have bands of varying color while others exhibit pleochroism, showing different colors when viewed from different directions.

Sunstones are mined from the surface from partially decomposed rock (with a pick and shovel) or from shallow pits and shafts dug to retrieve the rough.

Sunstone is mined in the US (Warner Valley, Oregon – the high copper content of Oregon Sunstones gives them their unique bright red orange colors), India, Canada, Tanzania, Tibet, Madagascar, Norway and Russia. Interestingly, some Sunstones from Madagascar display asterism (also known as the "star effect," this is caused by minerals reflecting a star of light back to the eye), which further accentuates Sunstone's natural sparkle.

Star Sunstone

One of the newest and most beautiful rare gems to be discovered, Tibetan Sunstone was first unearthed in 2002 in central Tibet on a cold and desolate mountain far from the reaches of modern civilization. It is also known as Andesine (for the location of this mineral's discovery in the lava flows of the Andes Mountains, Bolivia in 1841), Chinese Andesine, Tibetan Andesine, Andesine Labradorite and Red Labradorite. Initially bumping into some rough Tibetan Sunstone during a buying trip in East Africa, we were perplexed by its origin. Before we launched Tibetan Sunstone, its real origin remained a closely guarded or deliberately confused secret. While many incorrectly claim that the Democratic Republic of Congo is the source of this gemstone, using our network of gemstone contacts around the globe, we were able to get to the bottom of this modern gem mystery. Tibetan Sunstone is characterized by a swirling mix of coppery oranges, honeys, ambers, lemons and limes with a beautiful glittering sunlight effect caused by tiny copper inclusions. While the copper inclusions in Tibetan Sunstone are predominantly orange, they often disperse a fiery multitude of electric colors. With such an attractive blend of shimmering colors, Tibetan Sunstone has a unique appearance unlike any other gemstone.

Color Change Andesine in different lighting conditions

At GemsTV we use the name "Andesine" to differentiate the top quality bright red transparent

SUNSTONE:	Aventurescence
Origins:	Madagascar, India, Tibet & US
Colors Found:	Orange, red & yellow
Family:	Feldspar
Hardness:	6.00 - 6.50
Refractive Index:	1.53 - 1.55
Relative Density:	2.62 - 2.65

SUNSTONE

material (the top 1 - 3% of mining production) from regular Tibetan Sunstone. Similar to Paraiba Tourmaline (but differently colored), the red color of Andesine is due to the presence of copper. Andesine of this quality is extremely rare, and similar to its Feldspar cousins, Labradorite and Moonstone, most gem quality Tibetan Sunstone is coveted primarily for their blended colors. Andesine finally puts Feldspar in the same class as the very best the gem kingdom has to offer and in our opinion, this vivid red gem has set a new standard for beauty, not just for red Sunstone, but for any red gem. Similar to Alexandrite, the color change variety of Chrysoberyl, in extremely rare specimens Andesine can also display the color change effect. In daylight it is green while in incandescent light (or at night) it is a coppery red. Green Andesine, without a color change, is also available from this deposit. Nevertheless, supply of both Andesine and Tibetan Sunstone is erratic and very limited, making this beautiful rare gemstone even more collectible. Even given the slow and tedious methods employed, geologists estimate that the Tibetan deposit may only have a useful life of approximately 2 years.

Tibetan Sunstone is somewhat similar to Masai Sunstone from Tanzania. First found by a young Masai man on tribal grazing lands near Arusha in 2000, Masai Sunstone's basic red orange color mimics the bright hues of the Masai people's dress. Since the Masai have found several of East Africa's gem deposits (Tsavorite and Tanzanite), it is fitting that at least one of their gem discoveries carries their tribal name.

TANZANITE

Displaying an aurora of stunning royal blues, violets, indigos, lilacs, periwinkles, and ultramarines, Tanzanite's popularity is well deserved. Demand for Tanzanite has rocketed in recent years, outstripping sales of all other colored gemstones, with the exception of Sapphire. A thousand times rarer than Diamonds and with a little over a decade of mine life remaining, Tanzanite is the fashion gem of the millennium.

Legends and lore

The romance of Tanzanite begins in the arid Merelani foothills of Mount Kilimanjaro. Born of fire, Tanzanite's beauty remained secret to Tanzania's nomadic Masai until 1967. Legend has it that a short lived grass fire caused by a lightening strike was the first catalyst that turned burgundy violet surface pebbles of Zoisite (Tanzanite's gemological name) into the vibrant blues spotted by Masai herdsmen. While wonderfully romantic, it is now generally regarded as unlikely that enough heat could be generated by a grass fire to affect such a dramatic transformation.

In reality, the story of Tanzanite's discovery is as fascinating as the gem. While it is not known exactly who first found Tanzanite, the most popular story is that a local tribesman, Ali Juuyawatu discovered a translucent Tanzanite crystal at the base of Mount Kilimanjaro, sharing his find with a local prospector named Manuel D'Souza. D'Souza was actually searching for Rubies in the region and initially thought he'd discovered a new source of Sapphires. However, their multitude of blues and complex composition soon revealed Tanzanite's true identity to gemologists. Interestingly, the legendary Scottish geologist, Campbell R. Bridges, first discovered Tsavorite in Tanzania in 1967 during some Tanzanite consulting work for Tiffany & Co. and was the first person to bring Tanzanite to the US for identification by the GIA (Gemological Institute of America) Gem Trade Laboratory.

AAA Tanzanite & Diamond 18K Yellow Gold Ring

Tanzanite soon found its way to America, arriving at the New York-based jewelers Tiffany & Co. Henry B. Platt, great-grandson of Louis Comfort Tiffany and later President and Chairman of Tiffany & Co., was immediately enraptured by its beauty, but disturbed by its gemological name "Blue Zoisite." To him the name echoed "Blue Suicide." As with anything in fashion, it's all in the name, so this rare and exotic

AAA Tanzanite & Diamond 18K Yellow Gold Ring

TANZANITE

Tanzanite & Diamond 14K White Gold Ring

AAA Tanzanite & Diamond 18K Yellow Gold Ring

African gemstone was christened Tanzanite. At Tanzanite's official launch in October 1968, Platt remarked that it "was the most beautiful blue gemstone discovered in over 2,000 years."

Tanzanite's blue-purple fire soon took the fashion world by storm and was heralded "the gemstone of the 20th century." Demand for Tanzanite jewelry grew dramatically as its global appreciation increased, and in 1998 and 1999 Tanzanite was proclaimed the world's best selling colored gemstone.

While Tanzanite was adopted as one of December's official birthstones in 2002 (the first time the list changed since 1912), it is increasingly regarded as the ideal gem to celebrate new life and new beginnings. This belief has its roots in Masai tradition, where blue is believed to be a sacred spiritual color and bestowed in the form of blue beads and robes to women who have borne children. Today, this tradition has evolved, with Masai chiefs giving Tanzanite to wives on the birth of a baby. This gift is believed to bless their child with a healthy, positive and successful life.

Tanzanite continues to be all the rage in contemporary jewelry. Tom Ford, formerly "enfant terrible" of the Paris and Milan fashion house Gucci, once dominated the catwalks with a collection modeling exotic blue gems, including Tanzanite.

At the 2004 Oscars, Eileen Penn, mother of OSCAR® winner Sean Penn, stole the limelight from her son with a stunning Tanzanite and Diamond cross pendant.

Just the facts

A key ingredient in Tanzanite's success is that it exhibits more shades of blue than a clear midnight sky due to a phenomenon call pleochroism, whereby different colors are seen in different directions of the gemstone. Frequently, Tanzanite exhibits a color shift from the more bluish hues under daylight, to pinkish violets under incandescent light (candlelight). Most of the time, you can actually see both colors simultaneously; this is especially true in larger carat sizes where Tanzanite's colorful brilliance intensifies.

Tanzanite is also coveted because of its rarity. Tanzanite's production is slowly but surely decreasing and many experts are of the opinion that Tanzanite will disappear in years to come. This has led to Tanzanite gaining considerable notoriety; after all, the

Tanzanite… a thousand times rarer than Diamonds.

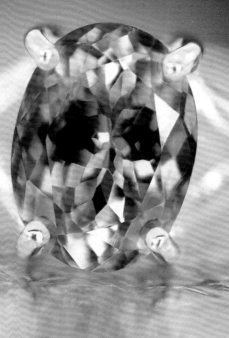

TANZANITE

AAA Tanzanite & Diamond
18K Yellow Gold Pendant

Tanzanite

TANZANITE:	December's birthstone
Origins:	Tanzania
Colors Found:	Shades of lilac, blue & purple as well as fancy colors
Family:	Zoisite
Hardness:	6.50 - 7.00
Refractive Index:	1.68 - 1.72
Relative Density:	3.35

desire to own something beautiful and unique has always been a decisive factor in fashion. Tanzanite is exclusively mined in East Africa in an area of Tanzania known as Merelani. The conditions involved in Tanzanite's formation 585 million years ago saw the random incorporation of vanadium during an event so unique it is often described as a geological phenomenon. Some experts even go as far as to maintain that the chance of Tanzanite occurring elsewhere is one in a million.

The Tanzanite deposits are hosted in metamorphic rocks, marbles and schists that belong to the Mozambique Belt (Rift Valley). The deposits run through the low hills of Merelani that rise from the hot Sanya plains, close to Mount Kilimanjaro. Running at an angle of 41 degrees to the surface, the deposit line or horizon periodically folds over itself, creating pockets of Tanzanite.

Barely covering 8 square miles, the Tanzanite mining area has been divided into four different sections known as "blocks" (lettered A, B, C & D) that have been allotted to different mining groups. While the largest scale and most sophisticated techniques used in Tanzanite mining take place in C block, the per ton yields for rough Tanzanite in C block average only 22 carats (4.4 grams) per processed ton!

Representing less than 1% of all Tanzanite mined, AAA Tanzanite is characterized by intensely deep purple blues and can be likened to an old French wine of an impossibly hard to obtain vintage. Interestingly, the D block section has earned the reputation for supplying the majority of AAA Tanzanite. AAA Tanzanite is the very best quality Tanzanite sold at GemsTV.

Tanzanite typically starts its life as bluish burgundy crystals that are heated to reveal their vibrant lilac, violet and blue colors. Occasionally, this process produces highly coveted and extremely rare fancy colors (Pink Tanzanite, Green Tanzanite, Ultramarine Tanzanite, Multi Color Tanzanite, etc.). Possessing all the qualities of regular Tanzanite, these colored varieties are far less common and are highly coveted by collectors. In gemology, the technically correct name for these gems is "(Color Prefix) Zoisite." However, Colored Tanzanite is generally accepted in the marketplace due to the gem's popularity and because this name specifies an origin.

Tanzanite exudes sophistication, individuality and self confidence. Lavish Tanzanite jewelry is suited to all ages, emphasizing the nonconformity of the young

TANZANITE

and the sophistication of the mature. However, Tanzanite is rare and growing rarer by the moment. Apart from the sheer pleasure of owning one of the 20th century's most spectacular gemstone discoveries, those fortunate to already own a Tanzanite or to purchase one before the only known deposit is depleted, truly are custodians of this spectacular gem whose legacy will be to pass it on as an heirloom to coming generations.

Tanzanite's wonderful colors, clarity and range of imaginative cuts lends itself to prominent display. Fashionable drop-earrings and pendants accentuate Tanzanite to the fullest, but Tanzanite is most popularly featured as large carat-sized solitaires mounted into prominent ring settings, showing off its scintillating colors to full effect.

TEKTITE (MOLDAVITE)

Moldavite 14K Yellow Gold Ring

Moldavite

TEKTITE:	Extraterrestrial gem
Origins:	Australia, Austria, China, Czech Republic, Germany, Laos, Malaysia, Philippines, Thailand & Vietnam
Colors Found:	Black & green
Family:	Tektite
Hardness:	5.50 - 6.50
Refractive Index:	1.48 - 1.50
Relative Density:	5.50 - 6.50

We are not alone! Since the beginning of time the curiosity of humankind has been aroused by the descent of "shooting stars" or meteorites into our world. So catch a falling star as we discover the mystery behind this extraterrestrial gemstone…

Tektite comes from the Greek word "tektos," meaning molten and was the name given by Edward Suess, a highly regarded professor at the University of Vienna.

A meteor is a small particle from space that appears as a bright light that completely burns up before it hits the ground. However, a meteorite is a meteor that is large enough to reach the ground without burning up completely. Frequently exploding on impact, throwing pieces of rare and highly sought after meteorite debris over a large area, these incredibly scarce and collectible gems are perfect for anyone fascinated by outer space.

Just the facts

Collectively known as Tektites, they are assigned specific names based on their location. For example, Moldavites, named after the river Moldu in the Czech Republic are found in this country as well as Austria and Germany, Australites are from Australia, Philippinites are from the Philippines and southern China, Malaysianites are from Malaysia, and Indochinites are from Thailand, Burma, China, Laos and Vietnam.

Considered to be gemstones from space, Tektites are fragments of natural glass that are formed from meteorite impacts with our planet. Tektites come in two forms. The more typical "splash form" Tektites have rounded aerodynamic shapes such as spheres, teardrops, dumbbells and disks, while "layered" Tektites are usually only found in southeast Asia and have blocky, fragmental shapes and often display compositional layering.

Some Tektites are smooth, but others have rough, strongly eroded surfaces. Most Tektites are jet black, but Moldavites are dark to bottle green and are usually the most suitable for faceting. Tektites look similar to Obsidian, which is a result of volcanic lava coming into contact with water, but they are differentiated by their color and chemical composition.

Tektites are only found in a few regions on earth (called Tektite strewn fields) and are, in most cases, associated with young impact craters on or near land.

TIGER'S EYE

Tiger's Eye is the best known variety of chatoyant Quartz (or Cat's Eye Quartz). Tiger's Eye, with its bands resembling the eye of a tiger, received its name due to this similarity. Tiger's Eye is also called Crocidolite Cat's Eye or African Cat's Eye. Tiger's Eye has rich yellow and golden brown stripes, with a fine golden luster when polished.

Legends and lore

Coveted since antiquity, Roman soldiers wore Tiger's Eye for protection in battle. Due to its appearance, in the ancient world Tiger's Eye was thought to be all seeing, offering protection during travel, and strengthening of convictions and confidence.

Many legends say that wearing Tiger's Eye is beneficial for health and spiritual well-being. Legend also says it is a psychic protector, great for business and aids in achieving clarity of mind.

Today, crystal healers use Tiger's Eye for focusing the mind.

Just the facts

Quartz gemstones are commonly separated into two groups based on the size of their individual crystals. The macrocrystalline Quartz (large crystal) group includes many popular gemstones such as Tiger's Eye, Amethyst, Ametrine and Citrine. Cryptocrystalline Quartz includes species whose individual crystals are too small to be easily distinguished. Apart from being a variety within the group, Chalcedony is also a catchall term to describe cryptocrystalline Quartz and includes many gems that have been coveted since antiquity.

Tiger's Eye is a pseudomorph (the result of one mineral replacing another) that contains oriented fibers of crocidolite that have been replaced by silica.

Tiger's Eye displays chatoyancy (a vertical luminescent band like that of a cat's eye). While Tiger's Eye typically has lustrous alternating yellow or brown bands, varieties of chatoyant Quartz include a blue-green variety called Hawk's Eye Quartz, a greenish-gray variety called Cat's Eye Quartz and a reddish brown variety called Bull's Eye Quartz or Ox Eye Quartz. Cutting is crucial with Tiger's Eye because the rough crystals reveal little or nothing of the exciting chatoyancy of the finished gem.

Golden Tiger's Eye 14K Yellow Gold Men's Ring

Tiger's Eye

TIGER'S EYE:	Chatoyancy
Origins:	Australia, Brazil, India, Namibia & South Africa
Colors Found:	Blue-green, golden brown, green-gray & reddish brown
Family:	Quartz
Hardness:	7.00
Refractive Index:	1.55
Relative Density:	2.65

TOPAZ

London Blue Topaz 14K Yellow Gold Ring

Sky Blue & White Topaz 14K Yellow Gold Ring

Swiss Blue Topaz

The origin of the name Topaz generates confusion, as some references point to the Sanskrit word "tapaz," meaning fire, while others believe it is named after Zeberget, an island in the Red Sea that the Greeks called Topazius, the ancient source of Peridot. While some sources think this was due to ancient confusion between Topaz and Peridot, it now appears more likely that this name might have come from confusion with the Greek word "topasin," which means to guess or conjecture, possibly in reference to the way fisherman sometimes lost the island in fog. Regardless, in history the name was not consistently or specifically applied (it was once used to describe most yellow gems) and sometimes Topaz and Peridot are mentioned as being the same and sometimes different. Interestingly, in the famous book "The Curious Lore of Precious Stones," the esteemed gemologist George Frederick Kunz (1856–1932) states that these two gems are the same species.

Topaz is an inherently romantic gem and features regularly in the titles of romance novels and honeymoon destinations. Its name indicates beauty, rarity and wealth, and imparts a sense of timelessness.

While the golden yellow and blues of Topaz are the most widely known, Topaz actually comes in a diverse array of striking colors. This combined with its beauty and durability, makes Topaz jewelry ideal for all occasions.

Legends and lore

Many ancient traditions and beliefs have created a brilliant history for Topaz. Like Peridot, the Egyptians called Topaz the "gem of the sun," believing it was colored by the golden glow of their sun god Ra and thus a powerful protector from harm.

Greeks and Romans also associated the golden crystals with their sun god, Jupiter. They believed the gem increased their strength and could neutralize enchantments.

Topaz is mentioned in the Bible as being one of the "stones of fire" (Ezekiel 28:13-16) that were given to Moses and set in the breastplate of Aaron (Exodus 28:15-30). Topaz is also one of the twelve gemstones set in the foundations of the city walls of Jerusalem (Revelations 21:19) and associated with the Apostle Matthew.

Bushmen in Africa used Topaz in healing ceremonies and rituals to connect with ancestral spirits.

In medieval courts, kings, judges and other noble persons were often presented with an engraved Topaz to win favor and cultivate positive relationships.

If you are on a journey of spiritual change, Topaz is believed by crystal healers to make an excellent companion. It apparently teaches you to trust in the universe, aiding you to fully recognize the magical laws of attraction, increasing your ability to manipulate them.

Once believed to make you invincible during danger, Topaz is also believed by some crystal healers to strengthen confidence and to help you make correct decisions by giving you the courage to follow through on choices, thereby changing dreams into reality.

Meditations with Topaz are believed by some to help awaken sleeping talents and illuminate co-creative energies.

Just the facts

Mined from both host rock and alluvial deposits, its unique crystal structure makes Topaz a hard and dense gemstone. Because of this, pure colorless Topaz has often been mistaken for Diamond. Weighing 1,680 carats, the huge Braganza gemstone mounted into the Portuguese crown jewels was originally thought to be a Diamond - in fact it is a beautiful clear Topaz.

A hydrous aluminum fluorosilicate, Topaz is usually formed in granitic pegmatites and in Quartz veins.

Glacier Topaz™

Blue Topaz

As well as the renowned Sky Blue Topaz, the more intense coloring of Swiss Blue and London Blue Topaz are also becoming increasingly popular.

Glacier Topaz™

A unification of fire and ice, Glacier Topaz™ mixes the pure clear whites of glacier ice with a fiery brilliance and luster reminiscent of Diamonds. Sourced from Russia's frozen wildness, Glacier Topaz™ is a stunning new gemstone exclusive to GemsTV.

Mined from the same region as Russian Alexandrite and Siberian Emerald, Glacier Topaz™ is yet another testament to the quality of Russian gemstones recently unearthed by our tireless gem hunters. Glacier

Cherry Topaz & White Topaz 18K Yellow Gold Ring

TOPAZ

*Champagne Topaz & White Topaz
14K Yellow Gold Ring*

Moonlight Topaz & White Topaz 14K Yellow Gold Ring

TOPAZ:	November's birthstone
Origins:	Brazil, Mozambique, Nigeria & Russia
Colors Found:	Various
Family:	Topaz
Hardness:	8.00
Refractive Index:	1.60 - 1.63
Relative Density:	3.50 - 3.60

Topaz™, arguably Topaz at its most pure, requires only cutting and faceting to reveal its hidden beauty.

Glacier Topaz™ is mined at one location on the planet, the famous Murzinka mines (named after the Ostyak's Prince Murzin) in the Ural Mountains, Russia. Active for well over a century, the Murzinka mines produce some of the world's finest Topaz, a gemstone for which Russia was once famous. While Brazil is today the recognized powerhouse for Topaz, Russian Topaz is relatively difficult to source, particularly with respect to the pure natural perfection embodied by Glacier Topaz™.

The miners work the deposits of the Murzinka granite pegmatite fields by tunneling up to 98 feet below the earth's surface in an effort to carefully extract Topaz crystals directly from the host rocks of the lucrative Mokrusha vein. Painstaking work, only a very small percentage of all the Murzinka Topaz mined has the necessary purity to warrant the distinction of being called Glacier Topaz™.

Imperial Topaz

At the height of Imperial Russia's power, orange pink Topaz was brought from Brazil to decorate the jewelry of the Tzarina. Since then, these colors have been known as Imperial Topaz and even today remain one of the most coveted varieties. Interestingly, some sources dispute this legend and state that Imperial Topaz was named in honor of Emperor Don Pedro of Brazil.

Mystic Topaz

Displaying a flaming kaleidoscope of colors, Mystic Topaz (also known as Mystic Fire Topaz, Rainbow Topaz, Titanium Topaz, Alaskan Topaz and Caribbean Topaz) is one of the 20th century's most beautiful new gemstones. First appearing in September 1998 at the Hong Kong Jewelry Fair, the popularity of Mystic Topaz increased dramatically when it was exhibited at the Tucson Gem Show in 2003.

Mystic Topaz is produced using the physical vapor deposition (PVD) coating process. Applied to top quality natural White Topaz, the treatment is permanent with normal wear (please see page 197 for more information on the PVD process). This process can induce an iridescent appearance, whose colors range depending on the light source and the viewing angle relative to both the gem's surfaces and the light source.

While Mystic Topaz displays a wide variety of scintillating celestial, earthly and oceanic hues all in one gemstone, the PVD process also produces a range of popular new Topaz colors including Red Topaz, Magenta Topaz, Flamingo Topaz, Twilight Topaz, Cornish Blue Topaz, Moonlight Topaz, Canary Topaz, Kiwi Topaz and Neptune Topaz.

TOURMALINE

Boasting a colorful and romantic history, Tourmaline rivals all but the most unique gems as it is found in an incredible array of gorgeous colors. Coming in a palette of over 100 different hues, Tourmaline is one of the world's most diverse gemstones. This has resulted in the nickname "the chameleon gem," which is doubly appropriate when you consider that one major source of Tourmaline is Madagascar, home to more than half of the world's chameleon species!

The name Tourmaline comes from the Sinhalese word "turmali," meaning mixed, due to a historical tendency for it to be confused and then mixed with other gem varieties.

Legends and lore

Sri Lanka (formerly Ceylon) was also partly responsible for Tourmaline's reappearance in Europe when Tourmaline gems were sold to Dutch traders who imported them to the west in the 15th century.

The Dutch, aside from admiring Tourmaline for its beauty, first discovered that this gem, like Quartz, possessed a unique property. Tourmaline when heated or rubbed creates an electrical charge, becoming a magnet that attracts lightweight materials.

A monarch particularly enchanted by Tourmaline was the Empress Dowager Tz'u Hsi, the last Empress of China. She loved Tourmaline so much, and was so wealthy, that she bought almost a ton of it!

Just the facts

While Tourmalines occur in large crystal sizes, Tourmaline of sufficient beauty to be set into jewelry is not available in great abundance. Because of their size, crystals are usually cut into long rectangular shapes following the axis of the crystal.

Tourmaline crystals occur in granitic pegmatite veins occurring in the great gem mining districts of Minas Gerais in Brazil, and the east African countries of Kenya, Tanzania, Mozambique, Malawi and Madagascar.

In the summer of 1998 a new Tourmaline deposit was unearthed near the city of Ibadan in Nigeria, West Africa, proving to be one of the most significant Tourmaline discoveries in modern times.

Tourmaline is a group of mineral species. However, it's the mineral Elbaite (named after the island of Elba near Italy's west coast where it was discovered) that is

Paraiba Tourmaline & Diamond
18K Yellow Gold Ring

TOURMALINE

responsible for almost all of Tourmaline's most famous gem varieties. When used, the name "Elbaite" typically references Green Tourmaline, while the other color forms of Elbaite have their own specific color-related names.

Tourmaline very occasionally displays the cat's eye effect. Chatoyancy or the cat's eye effect is a reflection effect that appears as a single bright band of light across the surface of a gemstone.

All Tourmalines can display pleochroism, meaning that its color changes when viewed at different angles. However, this can vary from specimen to specimen. In some, this effect is hardly noticeable, while in others it is strongly apparent. To bring out the best color, gemstone cutters must take this into account when faceting Tourmaline.

Multi Color Tourmaline

Mentioned in early 20th century gemological texts, it was not until the 1970's that Multi Color Tourmaline lent its charm to jewelry. Treasured for the magnificent harmony of its two colors, Multi Color Tourmaline possesses a distinctive beauty created by chance.

Due to its complex chemical composition, Tourmaline occurs in many colors. Multi Colored Tourmaline occurs because of differences caused by environmental changes. At different times, various color-causing elements (iron, manganese, titanium, chromium and vanadium) were incorporated into the crystal, causing different color layers. Purposefully cut to showcase this feature, Multi Colored Tourmaline displays a gorgeous contrast between its colors, typically pink and green, in one gem.

Given the environmental changes endured by Multi Color Tourmaline, like many Tourmalines (Paraiba or Rubellite), inclusions are common. Far from being flaws, inclusions are a hallmark of authenticity that record a gem's natural relationship with the Earth.

Multi Color Tourmaline & Diamond
14K Yellow Gold Pendant

Multi Color Tourmaline should not be confused with Watermelon Tourmaline. Watermelon Tourmaline is a crystal with the inner part showing pink surrounded by green. They are typically thinly sliced in sections, like a loaf of bread and polished to show the "watermelon" effect.

Multi Color Tourmaline

TOURMALINE

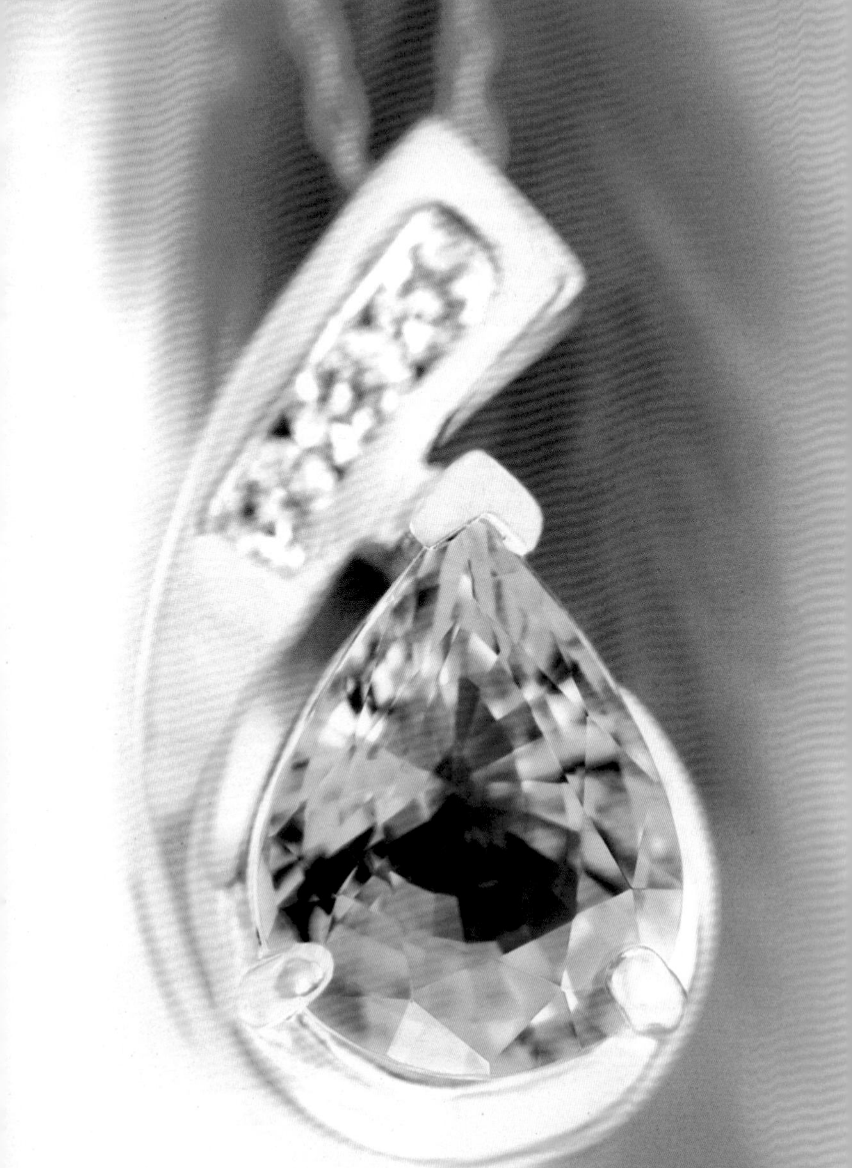

Green Tourmaline

Typically free from inclusions, Green Tourmaline offers gem consumers everything they want in an Emerald, but with more clarity.

Green Tourmaline has become very popular with collectors over recent years as they realize the true potential of this beautiful gem. Chrome Tourmaline is a scarcer variety of Green Tourmaline that bears chromium, the midas element responsible for producing particularly striking colors in a variety of gemstones.

Indicolite Tourmaline

Ranging in color from bright to deep blue, Indicolite Tourmaline is very rare and high quality specimens are highly collectible. Indicolite is strongly pleochroic (showing different hues when viewed from different directions). As Indicolite appears darker when viewed down the crystal, this must be taken into consideration when cutting, as a loss of transparency and brilliance can occur in darker specimens. The Romans reportedly used Indicolite, particularly in carved brooches that often bore the images of animals, as they believed it possessed strange occult powers. It was rediscovered in Europe in 1703 when the Dutch imported Indicolite they had discovered in Sri Lanka. Generally, only Indicolite less than 1 carat is available and as a result, bigger sizes are very rare and prized as special members of the Tourmaline family.

Green Tourmaline & White Topaz 14K Yellow Gold Ring

Paraiba Tourmaline

Paraiba Tourmaline is typically a small gem that displays electric swimming pool blues, neon peacocks and sizzling turquoises. Initially discovered at Mina da Bathalha, Paraiba, Brazil, it possesses a unique brilliance that allows the gem to glow and shine even when there is little light.

Indicolite

Named after the location of its first discovery, Paraiba, Brazil, the most interesting thing about this gem is that its name is more than just a location. Most Tourmalines get their gorgeous colors from traces of iron, manganese, chromium and vanadium, but Paraiba Tourmaline owes its spectacular colors to small amounts of copper, an element not typically found in Tourmaline. Paraiba Tourmaline also often contains manganese. When combined, the interaction between copper and manganese adds to the beautiful and fascinating colors displayed.

Paraiba Tourmaline

149

TOURMALINE

Paraiba Tourmaline 14K Yellow Gold Ring

Paraiba Tourmaline & Diamond 18K White Gold Ring

Prior to 1989, Mina da Batalha produced Tourmaline for almost 10 years but the crystals were too fractured or broken to be faceted. Heitor Dimas Barbos, the father of Paraiba Tourmaline, was convinced that better quality Tourmaline could be found. He started digging in abandoned mines near the village of Sao Jose da Batalha in early 1981. In autumn 1989 his persistence finally paid off when he discovered a tiny new vein of gem-quality crystals. By 1994 the relatively small mountain range had almost been leveled and exhausted in the hunt for Paraiba Tourmaline. Mining Brazilian Paraiba Tourmaline is laborious, unpredictable and erratic. Chipped by hand directly from host metamorphic rock (granitic pegmatite), the elusive narrow veins appear and disappear haphazardly, resulting in mines that resemble Swiss cheese, with a multitude of narrow shafts and interconnected tunnels up to 197 feet deep.

With the Brazilian deposit all but depleted, the race has been on to find these geological rarities elsewhere. Thankfully, Africa came to the rescue. The first new find was discovered in 2001 at the Edoukou Mine in Oyo, Nigeria, close to the border of Benin and in 2003 in Mozambique's Nampula (Mafucu Mine or Shalawa Mine) and Zambezia provinces. African Paraiba is believed to exist due to the theory of continental drift. Roughly 200 million years ago the earth's continents were joined together to form one gigantic super-continent called Pangaea. Comparing the silhouettes of Africa and South America, both fit like pieces in a jigsaw puzzle. This suggests they once belonged to a single landmass where similar geological conditions resulted in their formation. In contrast to the Brazilian deposit, African Paraiba Tourmaline is mined from alluvial deposits. Interestingly, the LMHC (Laboratory Manual Harmonization Committee) recently determined that as African Paraiba cannot be distinguished from their Brazilian counterpart by standard gemological tests, the "Paraiba" name is no longer origin specific, it is now only dependent on color, copper and manganese.

While mostly small sizes are extracted (less than 10 points) Paraiba Tourmaline from Mozambique has an average size of 2 carats, which is absolutely amazing considering the norm. Like Emeralds, inclusions are common in Paraiba Tourmaline, making its color the main beauty determinant. However, when Paraiba Tourmaline displays clean clarities, its rarity and value increase exceptionally. Its beautiful vivid colors have made Paraiba Tourmaline hugely popular within a short time. An uncommon color for the gem kingdom,

TOURMALINE

Paraiba Tourmaline even enchants those accustomed to seeing a wide variety of gems. One of the world's most desired gemstones, gem collectors the world over compete for new Paraiba Tourmaline. Paraiba Tourmaline is a gem whose impossible rarity is only surpassed by its unrivaled beauty - there is simply never enough to go around.

Rubellite Tourmaline

Rubellite's sensuous mélange is the personification of seduction; no other colors display its comparable flair. Whispering in passionate pinks and suggestive purples, Rubellite affords the perfect romance in an opulence of red. Rubellite, deriving its name from the Latin word "rubellus," meaning "coming from red" is a lustrous, reddish pink and purple-toned variety of Tourmaline. In the 17th century, the Tsar of Russia commissioned many items of gemstone jewelry to be made for the Imperial Crown Court. However, recently what were originally thought to be Rubies, in reality have been discovered to be Rubellite.

Extremely rare, Rubellite has taken the jewelry world by storm in recent years following the discovery of deposits in Madagascar and Nigeria. Madagascan Rubellite heralds from mines located 26 miles from the town of Betafo, in the Antananarivo province in Madagascar's central highlands. Interestingly, this deposit produces some truly unique Rubellites whose color is close to that of famous Rubies.

Rubellite & Diamond 18K Yellow Gold Ring

With the exception of Ruby and Noble Red Spinel, Rubellite is the only other gemstone that occurs in such a rich, dark red color. Similar to Emeralds, inclusions in Rubellite are common. The chemical elements that color Rubellite (manganese) actually cause a growing crystal to become internally flawed. The more the elements are present, the darker the red color, and the more imperfect the final crystal. It is therefore extremely rare to find a richly colored Rubellite that is internally clean. Rubellites also tend to have more natural inclusions because they are formed near the center of the crystal pocket, and thus receive more stress and pressure during their formation. Regardless, Rubellite is a durable gemstone, suited to everyday jewelry.

Rubellite

TOURMALINE:	October's birthstone
Origins:	Brazil, Kenya, Madagascar, Malawi, Mozambique, Nigeria, Sri Lanka & Tanzania
Colors Found:	Various
Family:	Tourmaline
Hardness:	7.00 - 7.50
Refractive Index:	1.62 - 1.64
Relative Density:	3.06

151

TURQUOISE

Turquoise 14K Yellow Gold Ring

Marcasite, Turquoise & Pearl 925 Silver Brooch

The name Turquoise is derived from the French "pierre turquois" meaning "Turkish Stone." This is because western Europeans mistakenly thought the gem came from Turkey. In fact it came from the Sinai Peninsula or the Alimersai Mountain in Persia (now Iran), which has been mining Turquoise since 5000 BC. In Persian, Turquoise is known as "ferozah," meaning victorious and it is the national gemstone of Iran to this day.

Legends and lore

Turquoise was one of the first gemstones ever mined, dating back to 6000 BC in Egypt's Sinai Peninsula.

In ancient times the Egyptians, Persians, Mongols and Tibetans all valued Turquoise highly. The first millennium AD saw a big increase in the popularity of Turquoise with both the Chinese and Native Americans becoming captivated by the blue stone.

Turquoise has been used for thousands of years as jewelry by the ancient Egyptians, who buried fine pieces with mummies. When the tomb of Queen Zer was unearthed in 1900, a Turquoise and Gold bracelet was found on her wrist, making this one of the oldest pieces of jewelry on earth!

The Persians preferred sky blue Turquoise and the term "Persian Turquoise" is now used as a color grade, not as a geographical indicator.

In Mexico, the Aztecs began mining Turquoise between 900-1000 AD, often fashioning it into elaborate masks.

The Anasazi people of America mined Turquoise in what are now Arizona, New Mexico and Colorado. The city of Chaco Canyon became very wealthy based on the Turquoise trade, which was often exchanged for the feathers of tropical birds. Turquoise from this area found its way around the trade routes of the American continent and has been unearthed as far away as the great Mayan city of Chichén Itzá in the Yucatán. By the 16th century, the cultures of the American southwest were using Turquoise as currency.

In North America, the Zuni people of New Mexico have created striking Turquoise jewelry set in silver, once believing these protected them from demons. The Navajo believed that Turquoise had fallen from the sky and thus also protected them from demons, while Apache warriors believed that wearing Turquoise improved their hunting prowess. Apache legend has it that if Turquoise was affixed to a bow, the arrows shot from it would always hit their mark. All these tribes believed that Turquoise brought good fortune and happiness.

European interest in Turquoise can be dated to around 500 BC when the people of Siberia began using the gem, but it did not make an impact on western European fashion until the late middle ages when trading with the Near and Middle East increased.

While the Chinese had some mines in their empire, they imported most of their Turquoise from Persians, Turks, Tibetans and Mongols. In Asia it was considered protection against the evil eye. Tibetans carved Turquoise into ritual objects as well as wearing it in traditional jewelry. Ancient manuscripts from Persia, India, Afghanistan, and Arabia report that the health of a person wearing Turquoise can be assessed by variations in the color of the gem. Turquoise was also thought to promote prosperity.

It is also believed that Turquoise helps one to start new projects and protects the wearer from falling, especially from horses! In Europe even today, Turquoise rings are given as forget-me-not gifts.

Montezuma's treasure, now displayed in the British Museum, includes a fantastic carved serpent covered by a mosaic of Turquoise. In ancient Mexico, Turquoise was reserved for the gods; it could not be worn by mere mortals.

TURQUOISE

Turquoise 925 Silver Watch

Just the facts

Turquoise, a hydrated phosphate of copper and aluminum, is prized as a gemstone whose intense blue color is often mottled with veins of brown limonite or black manganese oxide (commonly known as Spider Web Turquoise). Turquoise is almost always opaque and polished as cabochons but rare, translucent gems also exist.

Turquoise jewelry in the US has long been produced by Native Americans (Zuni and Navajo peoples). Today, Turquoise is prominently associated with Native American culture particularly Zuni bracelets, Navajo concha belts, squash blossom necklaces and thunderbird motifs. Native American jewelry with Turquoise mounted in or with silver is actually relatively new. Some believe this style of jewelry was unknown prior to about 1880, when a white trader persuaded a Navajo craftsman to make Turquoise and silver jewelry using coin silver.

Turquoise 925 Silver Bracelet

TURQUOISE:	December's birthstone
Origins:	Afghanistan, China, India, Iran & US
Colors Found:	Bluish green & sky blue
Family:	Turquoise
Hardness:	5.00 - 6.00
Refractive Index:	1.61 - 1.65
Relative Density:	2.60 - 2.80

ZIRCON

Ice Zircon™ 14K Yellow Gold Ring

*Orange Zircon & White Topaz
18K Yellow Gold Ring*

Zircon's name is either derived from the Arabic word "zarkun," meaning red, or a combination of the ancient Persian words "zar," meaning gold and "gun," meaning color. Despite this name, Zircon actually occurs in a myriad of colors.

Zircon's brilliant luster, fire and bright hues makes it an enjoyable addition to any jewelry collection.

Legends and lore

Zircon has been found in some of the most ancient archaeological sites.

Zircon has appeared in literature and the gem trade under a variety of names including Jargon (Yellow Zircon), Jacinth (Red Zircon), Matara Diamond (White Zircon), Starlite (Blue Zircon), Hyacinth (Blue, Yellow and Red Zircon) and Ligure.

Zircon is first mentioned in the ancient Indian tale of the Kalpa Tree. Described by Hindu poets as the ultimate gift to the gods, it was a bright glowing tree with bejeweled leaves of Zircon.

The gemstone of fiery starlight, Jewish legends say that Zircon was the name of the guardian angel sent to watch over Adam and Eve in the Garden of Eden.

Zircon is mentioned in the Bible (using the name Jacinth for its red variety) as being one of the "stones of fire" (Ezekiel 28:13-16) that were given to Moses and set in the breastplate of Aaron (Exodus 28:15-30). Zircon is also one of the twelve gemstones set in the foundations of the city walls of Jerusalem (Revelations 21:19) and associated with the Apostle Simon.

The Roman historian, Pliny the Elder, compared Blue Zircon's color to hyacinth flowers.

Traditionally, Zircon is a gem of purity and innocence. Zircon is believed to promote inner peace while providing the wearer with wisdom, honor and riches. Legend also has it that a Zircon's loss of luster is a warning of imminent danger.

Zircon's popularity grew dramatically in the 16th century when Italian artisans featured the gem in jewelry designs. In the 1880's Blue Zircon was widely used in Victorian jewelry.

Just the facts

Although Zircon's existence predates Cubic Zirconia by centuries, Zircon is often unfairly confused with Cubic Zirconia. Cubic Zirconia is a cheap, synthetic Diamond substitute that resembles colorless Zircon and has a similar sounding name. While Zircon may also be used as an excellent Diamond substitute, it is valuable in its own right.

The fire in Zircon, called dispersion, is caused by light entering the gemstone and separating into a prism of rainbow colors. Possessing dispersion approaching that of Diamond, the brilliance of Zircon is second to none. The Zircon cut, a variation of the Round Brilliant cut that adds eight extra facets to the pavilion, was designed to take advantage of these properties.

A very unique characteristic of Zircon is birefringence (doubly refractive), meaning that light splits into two rays as it passes through the gem. As a result, the back facets appear as double images, lending optical depth to the gem. Zircon also has an adamantine (Diamond-like) luster, lending further credence to its suitability as a Diamond substitute.

Zircon remains unscathed while other rocks and minerals melt and reform under the tremendous heat and pressure of continental shifts, mountain-building and violent asteroid impacts. Once only considered a Diamond alternative, Zircon is in fact incredibly ancient. A tiny fragment of Zircon discovered in Western Australia is the oldest known object on Earth at 4.404 billion years old (the Earth formed less than 150 million years earlier). Diamonds in comparison are quite young, a mere 3.3 billion years old.

Cambodia is arguably the world's premiere source for gorgeous Blue Zircon. Sixty two miles north of Angkor Wat, close to the Cambodian Thai border, are the mines of Preah Vihear. Remote, pristine and stunningly beautiful, Ratanakiri is another major center for Cambodian Zircon, yielding some of the world's finest Blue Zircon. Ratanakiri literally means "gemstone mountain." South of the city, a mining camp has been carved from the forest, where workers toil to extract Ratanakiri Zircon from narrow mine shafts that tap into an alluvial layer about 15 feet below the surface. Matt McNamara, one of GemsTV's presenters, visited several Ratanakiri Zircon mines in 2004 and 2007: "I was amazed to see the miners still using traditional mining techniques, which remain effective to this day. It's easy to forget how much work goes into unearthing these wonderful gems."

A unification of fire and ice, Ice Zircon™ mixes the pure clear whites of ice with a fiery brilliance and luster reminiscent of Diamonds. Proprietary to GemsTV, our Ice Zircon™ hails from Mahenge, Tanzania in East Africa.

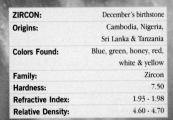

ZIRCON:	December's birthstone
Origins:	Cambodia, Nigeria, Sri Lanka & Tanzania
Colors Found:	Blue, green, honey, red, white & yellow
Family:	Zircon
Hardness:	7.50
Refractive Index:	1.93 - 1.98
Relative Density:	4.60 - 4.70

ZULTANITE

Zultanite & Diamond 14K Yellow Gold Ring

Zultanite in different lighting conditions displaying its characteristic color change

ZULTANITE:	Color change
Origins:	Turkey
Colors Found:	Various (see opposite)
Family:	Diaspore
Hardness:	6.50 – 7.00
Refractive Index:	1.70 – 1.75
Relative Density:	3.30 – 3.39

Astonishingly beautiful, sparklingly brilliant, durable and exceedingly rare, Zultanite's tranquil earthy colors have made it a rising star in fine jewelry. While an article in "Gems & Gemology" magazine (Winter 1994) indicated that supplies were promising, good quality gems have only recently become available. GemsTV is delighted to be the exclusive global outlet for this phenomenal gemstone.

First faceted in the late seventies, some jewelers previously traded this gem as "Diaspore," but these were typically finished by inexperienced cutters, resulting in poor quality. Zultanite is your guarantee that each gem has been optimally cut by some of the world's most experienced lapidaries. Zultanite was named in honor of the 36 sultans who founded the Ottoman Empire in Anatolia in the late 13th century. Its gemological name "Diaspore," comes from the Greek word "diaspora" meaning "to scatter." Diaspore was first discovered in 1801 in Mramorskoi, Kossoibrod, Ural Mountains, Russia.

Legends and lore

Some people believe Zultanite can assist in developing psychic power, astral force, ambition, intellect and desire.

Just the facts

Similar to Alexandrite, Zultanite can change from kiwi greens with canary flashes in sunlight (candescent) to raspberry purplish-pinks in candlelight (incandescent). Zultanite can also display khaki greens, sage greens, cognac pinks, pinkish champagnes, rich champagnes and gingers. Zultanite's darker pinks are caused by higher manganese content. While just wearing Zultanite unveils its breathtakingly diverse colors, one of its most unique characteristics is that Zultanite's best color change is not dependent on dark tones. Some Zultanite also possess the coveted cat's eye effect (chatoyancy).

Like Tanzanite, Zultanite is so rare that it is only found in one location worldwide. Zultanite is mined by hand in Turkey's Anatolian Mountains (Milas county of Mugla) at a height of over 4,000 feet, 7 miles away from the village of Selimiye. But its rarity isn't just dictated by its natural scarcity and remoteness. With up to 90% of the crystal lost during cutting due to perfect cleavage (like Diamonds, Zultanite crystals can split apart in one direction) and orienting the crystal for color change, its very low yield is one of the reasons Zultanite is so rare, especially in larger sizes (over 5 carats).

MORE GEMS

While we don't have enough space to include every gemstone in this guide, simply visit **www.GemsTV.com** for more information on the following varieties:

Amazonite
Amblygonite
Ammolite
Anapaite
Anglesite
Apophyllite
Aragonite
Axinite
Azurite
Barite
Bastnaesite
Bloodstone
Boracite
Burbankite
Bustamite
Calcite
Cassiterite
Celestite
Charoite
Chrysocolla
Cinnabar
Cobalt Calcite
Creedite
Danburite
Datolite
Dolomite
Dumortierite
Ekanite
Enstatite
Epidote
Euclase

Eudialyte
Fossils
Genthelvite
Hauyne
Hematite
Hemimorphite
Herderite
Hexagonite
Howlite
Idocrase
Leifite
Magnesite
Manganotantalite
Mawsitsit
Mellite
Meteorites
Milarite
Monazite
Montebrasite
Mookite
Natrolite
Nuummit
Oligoclase
Parisite
Pectolite (Larimar)
Petalite
Phenakite
Pollucite
Pyroxmangite
Quartzite
Remondite

Rhodonite
Rutile
Sard
Sardonyx
Scheelite
Senarmontite
Serandite
Shortite
Siderite
Sinhalite
Smithsonite
Sodalite
Spectrolite
Sphalerite
Spodumene
Staurolite
Sugilite
Tanolite™
Thaumasite
Tremolite
Tugtupite
Unakite
Villiaumite
Willemite
Wulfenite

UNDERSTANDING GEMSTONES

The beauty, rarity and historical mystique of gems are timeless. Their richly diverse varieties and colors come in a kaleidoscopic array that puts Diamonds to shame. However, before you make a purchase, you will need a basic understanding of gems.

Understanding and appreciating the value of gems is essential to making a successful and rewarding purchase. Regardless of the gem variety you're buying, there are a few constant rules to bear in mind.

What is a gem?

For decades, the Gemological Institute of America (GIA) has taught their students that "gems are specimens of minerals (i.e., most gemstones are generally solid crystalline minerals formed by the earth's geological processes) or organics (i.e., materials formed by organic life processes such as animals, e.g., Pearls; or trees, e.g., Amber) used for personal adornment that possess the attributes of beauty, rarity and durability." The GIA states that all three of these attributes must be present - a gem lacking in one or more of these attributes risks losing its status as a gem.

You may have heard about the 4 C's related to valuing gemstones: color, cut, carat weight and clarity. While gemstone professionals and connoisseurs the world over rely on these factors, we'll also cover other elements that also need to be taken into consideration when purchasing colored gemstones.

Color

Understandably, color is the single most important factor when evaluating colored gems. Generally, the more attractive a gem's color, the higher the value. Bright, rich and intense colors are generally coveted more than those that are dark or light. However, there are exceptions such as Morganite and Rose de France Amethyst. Although specific color hues can affect the prices of gems, as color is subjective, personal preferences are also very important. The colors seen should ideally remain attractive regardless of prevailing light conditions. Whether viewed indoors, outdoors, by day or by night, a gem should always remain beautiful.

The mixing of color hues into combinations, such as purple blue in Tanzanite and bright blue green in Apatite is attractive and value-enhancing. Many gems also have specific expressions to denote the very top

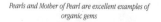

Pearls and Mother of Pearl are excellent examples of organic gems

colors found within a species (e.g., Cornflower Blue Sapphire). Such terms relate to the most desirable colors to be found within a gem species (i.e., colors that cannot be bettered).

The elements that give most gemstones their color are termed "idiochromatic" or "self colored" if they are an intrinsic ingredient of the gem (i.e., the color results from a coloring element that is always incorporated into the crystal structure of the mineral) or "allochromatic" or "other colored" if they are trace elements (i.e., small amounts of an element that is not part of the normal crystal causes the color). However, color in some gemstones, such as Colored Diamonds and Blue Topaz, are caused by "color centers." These are imperfections in crystals that cause color by absorption of light.

Cut

Unlike Diamonds, colored gems possess variable optical properties and are not cut to a uniform ideal. A well-cut colored gem exhibits even color, an acceptable number of inclusions for the type, good brilliance and shows the majority of carat weight when viewed from the top. As gemstones are nature's creations, cutting is often a juggling act between carat weight retention and beauty.

As Paraiba Tourmaline is colored by trace amounts of copper, it is an allochromatic gemstone

Broadly, the styles of gem cutting can be divided into faceted gems (i.e., gems with geometrically-shaped flat polished faces) and non-faceted gems (i.e., those gems that do not have geometrically-shaped flat polished faces such as cabochons).

Carat weight

Gemstone weight is measured in carats. This archaic unit of measurement originates from the traditional use of carob seeds to weigh gems in the bazaars of the Middle East and Asia. Carob seeds were used because of their consistent size and shape. In 1907 in Europe and in 1913 in the US, carat weight was standardized as one fifth of a gram (i.e., one carat is the equivalent of 0.20 grams). Gemstones less than 1 carat are often measured by dividing the carat weighed into 100 smaller units known as points. For example, a 50 point gemstone can also be described as half a carat and a 25 point gemstone can also be described as a quarter of a carat.

Always shades of green due to iron in their crystal structure, Peridot are idiochromatic gemstones

The term carats is often confused with "karats." Karat is a measurement of gold purity and has no

UNDERSTANDING GEMSTONES

relationship to the term carats, other than the fact that they both originate from the use of carob seeds, which in this case was used to weigh the alloys added to gold.

Generally, as the weight of a gem increases, so does its price per carat. Large gems are always rarer than smaller ones, so per carat prices rise exceptionally. For example, a 3 carat Ruby is always worth far more than three 1 carat Rubies of the same quality. The only time the combined weight of smaller gems costs more than a singular gem of the same carat weight is when the labor cost of applying all the facets to the individual gems outweighs the difference in price.

Gemstone prices also increase rapidly when in excess of certain key weights. For example, a 2.01 carat Ruby has a higher price tag than a 1.99 carat Ruby, despite a negligible difference in actual size. Gem pricing is said to suffer a "nonlinear scale of increments." To put this into context, a 16 carat Ruby sold at Sotheby's in New York in October 1988 for a staggering $3,630,000! If gem pricing was linear, that would make a similar 1 carat Ruby worth $226,875.

One 3 carat gemstone is usually worth more than three 1 carat gemstones

As gemstones are nature's creations, no two gemstones are absolutely identical. Therefore, the gem weights specified on the GemsTV certificate of authenticity is the MTGW (Minimum Total Gem Weight) used to create each jewelry design. Each specific handcrafted piece will most likely contain a higher gem weight.

If you are buying a gem with a rounded carat weight, make sure that the quality of the cut (i.e., beauty) has not been compromised to achieve a larger carat weight, as a reduction in beauty might reduce the value of the gem.

Clarity

Inclusions are a natural characteristic of Emeralds

Often adding character and individuality, most gems contain tiny natural features called inclusions. Mostly microscopic in nature, they are most easily glimpsed under magnification. Far from being flaws (i.e., in most textbooks inclusions are defined as internal flaws in a gemstone), inclusions are a fascinating hallmark of authenticity that record a gem's natural relationship with the earth.

The clarity of gems is determined by judging the amount and location of inclusions that can be seen. Basically, the higher the clarity grade, the higher the value of the gem. In general, inclusions that don't interfere with the brilliance, sparkle and fire of a gem don't affect the value. In some cases, inclusions can even increase a gemstone's beauty and value (e.g., asterism or the star effect).

UNDERSTANDING GEMSTONES

In transparent gems, the degree of transparency and light return (brilliance) is considered crucial. However, through market experience, we learn to expect certain degrees of clarity from certain gems. For example, Aquamarine is generally expected to be clean (no inclusions) and Emerald is expected to be hazy (with inclusions).

Country

The fifth C is "Country" of origin. Names of geographical locations should only be used when they denote the areas from which gemstones originate (for example, it is misleading to call a high quality Amethyst "Siberian" if it doesn't actually come from Siberia).

While there are exceptions, gemstones that are rich in history and folklore are generally more prized than those lacking historical connotations.

When specifying an origin, GemsTV undertakes a series of checks based on our experience to ensure that a gemstone displays the characteristics indicative of the origin specified. While GemsTV does everything possible to ensure that the origins we specify are correct, gemstone origin is considered a matter of opinion.

Conflict free

The sixth C is "Conflict" free. Any Diamonds purchased from GemsTV have been sourced from legitimate traders not involved in funding conflict and in compliance with the United Nations Resolutions (i.e., the Kimberley Process). You can learn more about the Kimberley Process on page 40 of this guide or by visiting **www.DiamondFacts.org**.

Based on personal knowledge and/or written guarantees provided by our suppliers, GemsTV guarantees that our gemstones have been purchased from legitimate sources not involved in funding conflict or terrorism.

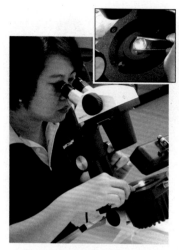

Microscopes and other gemological equipment are used on a daily basis at GemsTV

It is incorrect to call high quality Amethyst "Siberian" unless it actually comes from Siberia

UNDERSTANDING GEMSTONES

Mitsunari Yoshimoto, the bead gem buyer for GemsTV, negotiating

Durability

"The love of precious gemstones is deeply implanted in the human heart," George Kunz wrote in his book, "The Curious Lore of Precious Stones." "The cause of this must be sought not only in their coloring and brilliancy but also their durability." Kunz further wrote, "The sheen and coloration of precious stones are the same today as they were thousands of years ago and will be for thousands of years to come. In a world of change, this permanence has a charm of its own that was early appreciated."

A gemstone must be durable enough not to break or fade over years of wear. Its brilliance and beauty are expected to last for a very long time, even to the point where a gemstone will outlast its owners and be passed on to sons and daughters, who, in turn, will help maintain its status as a gem and awaken appreciation in the succeeding generations. While gems with better durability and resistance to wear are generally more highly prized than those of lesser durability, given proper care, all gemstone jewelry should be suitable to be passed down to many generations.

Durability is a combination of 3 properties:

1. **Hardness:** This is the ability of a gem to resist surface scratching. The hardest natural substance is Diamond. Second and third to Diamond is Corundum (Ruby and Sapphire) and then Topaz. Hardness is quantified on a scale of 1 to 10. Ten being the hardest and 1 the softest - it is a comparative not a relative scale. The minerals chosen set the levels of hardness. The system was devised in the 18th century by a Viennese mineralogist Friedrich Mohs and is named after him (i.e., Mohs' Hardness Scale).

2. **Toughness:** This is the ability of a gem to resist the development of fractures (i.e., random non-directional breakage) or cleavage (i.e., splitting along certain well-defined planes).

3. **Stability:** This is the ability of a gem to resist physical or chemical damage.

Diamonds may be the hardest gem, but they are not the toughest

Rarity

By their very definition, all gems are rare. Rarity can be described in three, often unrelated, ways:

1. Geological
2. Marketplace
3. Comparative

While scarcer gems are generally more highly prized than less scarce varieties, geological rarity doesn't always mean a gem has a higher value in the marketplace and vice versa. Beauty and marketing play a big part. Sometimes the geological rarity of a gem type jeopardizes commercial viability. Tsavorite Garnet is rarer than Emerald, and is frequently more beautiful, but because of its rarity, it cannot compete with Emerald in terms of the consumer perception of its value. Given the enormous Diamond stockpiles and new sources springing up around the world, when compared to many colored gemstones, Diamonds are not especially rare. Strict control of polished Diamonds on the market, combined with sophisticated consumer advertising, has elevated Diamonds to the extent that they are perceived as a rare and coveted product.

If a gem variety is so rare that it is essentially unknown to the general public, it is often classified as an "exotic gem." Gems such as Boracite, Childrenite and Simpsonite are extremely rare, attractive and durable, but they are unlikely to command prices appropriate to their rarity because few people are aware of their existence.

Pairs and suites

Pairs or suites of gems matched for color, clarity and cut are valued more highly per carat or per gem than single gems of the same quality. Given the rarity of many gems, a matching set is disproportionately hard to find and will command a higher per carat price than if each of the gems from the suite were sold separately.

A cluster of matching Tsavorite Garnets, a delightful green gem that is rarer than Emeralds

LUSTER, BRILLIANCE & FIRE

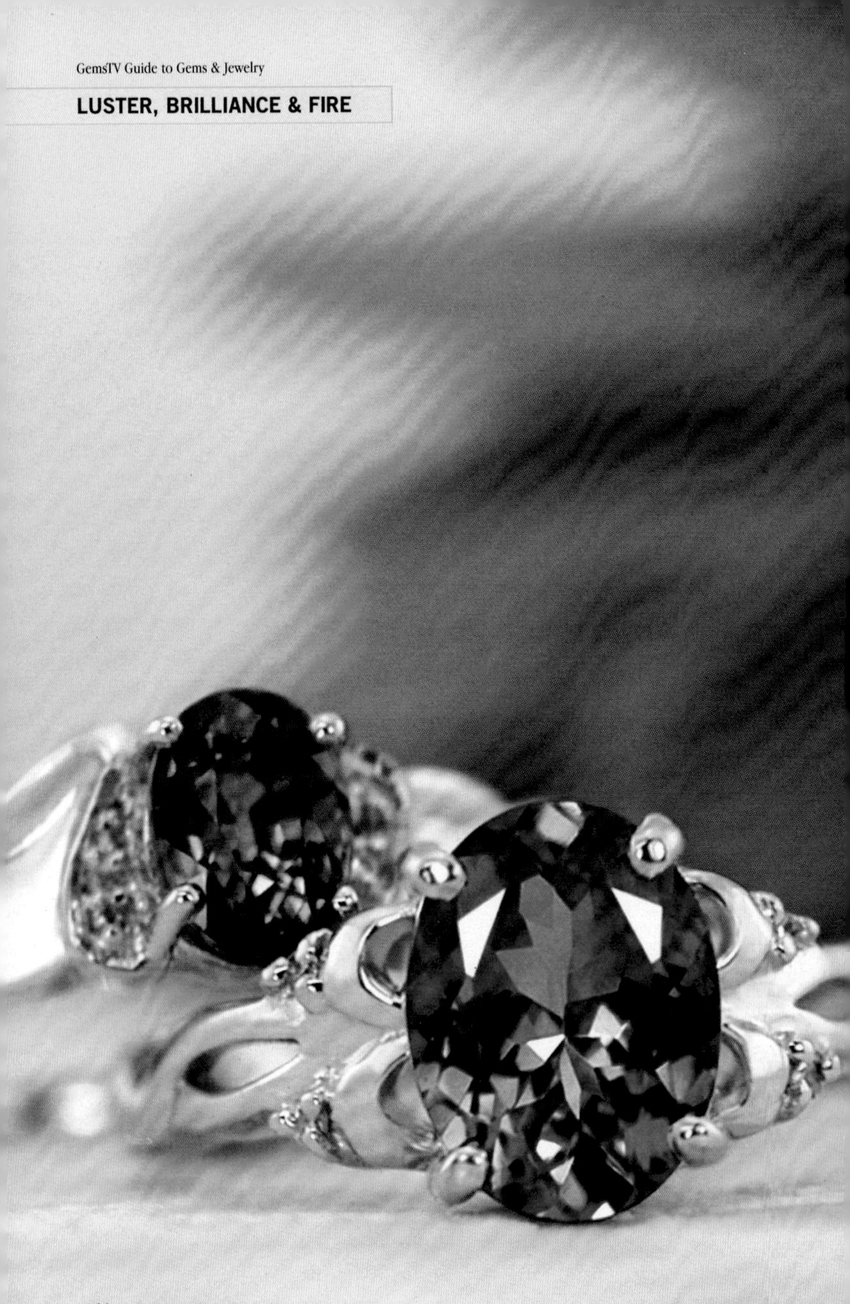

These frequently used terms to describe the visual appearance of the interaction between light and a gem are often confused and misused, sometimes even by experienced industry professionals! The following clears up the confusion, allowing you to understand exactly what you are seeing when you gaze upon your gemstone jewelry.

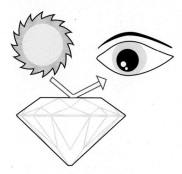

Luster is the surface reflection of light

Luster

Luster is the external reflection effect and is the amount of light that is reflected from a gem's surface.

If nearly all of the light that falls upon a gem is reflected, resulting in a very bright reflection, it is said to have a "high luster" (a mirror). If much of the light is absorbed by the gem, resulting in a dull reflection, it is said to have a "low luster" (a brick). Commonly used terms to describe luster include:

1. **Adamantine:** Very bright and reflective, almost metallic, luster as displayed by Diamond, Alexandrite and Demantoid Garnet. The descriptive term "sub-adamantine" is also sometimes used to describe the luster of gems with a bright luster other than Diamonds.

2. **Vitreous:** The luster seen in polished glass and in most transparent gemstones whose refractive indices fall within the middle range of values (e.g., Emerald and Tourmaline).

3. **Resinous:** Certain gems that have low refractive indices, like Amber, have a resinous luster.

4. **Silky:** Some fibrous minerals such as Gypsum and Malachite have a silky luster.

Due to their opacity, the high luster of Black Diamonds is easily visible

5. **Metallic:** This is the very high luster shown by metals such as gold and silver, and by gems such as Hematite and Pyrite.

6. **Pearly:** Pearls are composed of layers from which light is reflected at and near the surface.

Brilliance

Brilliance is the internal reflection effect and is the amount of light that is reflected from a gem's interior. Brilliance is dependent on a gem's optical properties (i.e., refractive index) and cutting (remember, colored gems are not cut to a uniform ideal). Brilliance also depends on transparency (determined by a gem's color and optical properties), clarity, polish, luster and wear.

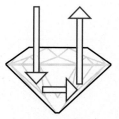

A well cut gem should maximize the light reflected through the top of the gem

LUSTER, BRILLIANCE & FIRE

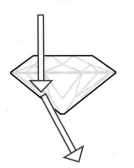

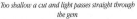

Too shallow a cut and light passes straight through the gem

Too deep a cut and the light will not be sufficiently returned to the top of the gem

Certain cutting angles allow the light to pass straight through the gem or to be deviated to the side. Accurate cutting to optimum angles will allow light to travel back towards the viewer when looking directly into the table facet.

Gems with low refractive indices (e.g., Quartz, Beryl, Iolite, etc.) are not usually cut to show maximum brilliance as a very steep pavilion would be required. This would make the resulting gems too deep to be set into jewelry.

It is important to note that not all gems have the same optimal cut. Although it is true that many gems demonstrate optimal brilliance when cut to the same proportions as a perfectly round brilliant cut Diamond, other gem types benefit from either deeper or shallower pavilions. Optimizing the cut (faceting) for each gem type is an art in itself. Gems that are not cut correctly, either through a lack of experience or due to the gem cutter aiming to maximize the carat weight, rather than extract maximum beauty, will mean that the gem will not display its optimum brilliance.

Fire

Fire (or dispersion), is the splitting of light into its component colors (i.e., red, orange, yellow, green, blue and violet light). As light passes from one medium to another its individual colors are bent by different amounts. The resulting effect to the eye is that the light no longer appears to be white, but appears as separate colors. Sphene, Demantoid Garnet, Diamond, Zircon and all gemstones of a large size exhibit fire. It is a desirable property in gemstones, adding both beauty and value.

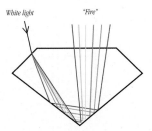

White light   *"Fire"*

When a gem splits light into its component colors it is said to have fire

Sphene is a rare gem whose fire is greater than Diamonds

The earth consists of elements made up of countless atoms. Most of these atoms are in orderly, solid arrangements. Materials with such orderly atomic arrangements are said to be crystalline and each different atomic arrangement is called a crystal structure (i.e., a regular, repeating, three-dimensional arrangement of bonded atoms). Most gems are crystalline (i.e., they possess a crystal structure). Atoms bond together most efficiently as orderly crystal structures and as a result, automatically try to pack into the most orderly structure possible. Crystalline materials can be either:

1. Comprised of a single piece of crystal. Single-piece crystals are termed macrocrystalline. Most gemstones fall into this category, such as Ruby, Sapphire, Amethyst and Tourmaline.

2. Comprised of a crystalline structure so fine that no distinct particles are recognizable under the microscope. Termed cryptocrystalline, examples include Jade, Agate and Chrysoprase.

Moonstone displaying its characteristic adularescence

Some gems exhibit unusual optical effects known as phenomena. These rare and beautiful effects often add value to gems. The cat's eye effect, the star effect and the color change effect are very popular phenomena and are highly coveted. It is the possession of different crystal structures offered by many gemstones that gives them their unique properties. Without these unique properties, our ancestors would have never valued them as unusual, rare, desirable or beautiful and, in turn, without them, our gemstone choices would be very limited.

Adularescence

Moonstone shows a blue-whitish opalescence (sometimes described as a "billowy" light and shimmer) that glides over the surface of the gem. Interference phenomena from the gem's layered structure are the cause of this effect.

Asterism

Also known as the star effect, this is a reflection effect that appears as two or more intersecting bands of light across the surface of a gem. It is usually created through reflection of light by thin fibrous or needle-like inclusions that lie in various directions. There are 6 ray, 4 ray and, rarely, 12 ray stars. Ruby and

Star Ruby

167

OPTICAL EFFECTS

Tibetan Sunstone displaying its characteristic aventurescence

Cat's Eye Chrysoberyl

Sapphire cabochons can sometimes very effectively show this phenomenon. Gemstones will produce this effect when:

1. The inclusions are long and needle-shaped.

2. The inclusions are in parallel arrangements in at least two different directions.

3. The inclusions are sufficiently abundant.

4. The gemstone is cut in such a way that the top is curved and the base is parallel to the direction in which the inclusions lie. To reveal asterism, the gemstone must be cabochon cut.

The quality and value of an asteriated gem is judged by:

1. The distinctiveness of its star.

2. The length and degree of straightness of each ray.

3. The strength and uniformity of the gem's color.

4. The position of the star. While typically centered, in some cases the star is deliberately off centered for artistic affect (e.g., non-round cabochons).

5. The gem's size and carat weight.

   Asterism (and chatoyancy) is most visible with direct light, such as a fiber optic light, penlight or another single beam of light, including direct sunlight. With diffused illumination, stars and cat's eyes are not as distinct (often a problem under TV studio lights).

Aventurescence

This is a colorful play of glittering reflections of small, plate or leaf-like metallic inclusions. Gemstones that display this phenomenon include Aventurine (after which the phenomenon is named) and Sunstone.

Chatoyancy

Also known as the cat's eye effect, this is a reflection effect that appears as a single bright band of light across the surface of a gemstone, similar to the slit eye of a cat. It is caused by the reflection of light by parallel fibers, needles or channels. Gemstones will show a chatoyant reflection when:

1. The inclusions are long and needle-shaped.

2. The inclusions are in parallel arrangement.

3. The inclusions are sufficiently abundant.

4. The gemstone is cut in such a way that the top is curved and the base is parallel to the direction in which the inclusions lie. To reveal chatoyancy, the gemstone must be cabochon cut.

One of the most coveted cat's eye is Cat's Eye Chrysoberyl - so much so, that if you just mention cat's eye, it is assumed to be in reference to Cat's Eye Chrysoberyl. All other cat's eye gems, such as those found in Tourmaline or Tiger's Eye, typically have an additional designation.

Color Change

Color change gems show different colors when viewed under two different light sources. This is due to the gem's absorption of different colors of the spectrum from different light sources. Examples of gemstones that display this phenomenon include Alexandrite, Color Change Sapphire and Color Change Garnet. The sensation of color change in gems depends upon certain basic requirements:

1. A source of white light.

2. Suitable modification to this light. Color change is dependent on pure light sources. With diffused illumination, the color change will not appear as dramatic.

3. The eye and brain to perceive and interpret the light.

Zultanite demonstrating a very dramatic and exceedingly rare color change

But exactly how is this color change effect caused? The light that we see mostly appears to be white - the human brain perceives it as a single color. However, through science we know that white light is made up of the individual colors of the spectrum; its components are combinations of Red, Orange, Yellow, Green, Blue and Violet light. Lights from different sources have different combinations or balances of these component colors. For example, pure bright sunlight has very strong blue components, while electric light is far richer in the red wavelengths, although it appears very similar to sunlight to our eyes. A small difference in the source of light can sometimes produce a very large difference in our perception of a gem's color.

The color change effect or "Alexandrite Effect" is a rare, beautiful and desirable property in gemstones. When light enters a gemstone it is usually white light. As the light passes through the gem, it absorbs some of the component colors of the spectrum. The

Ratanakiri Zircon's double refractivity lends it optical depth

OPTICAL EFFECTS

Fire Agate's iridescence breaks light into its spectral colors

Play of color in Lightning Ridge Black Opal

Iridescence in Mystic Topaz

resulting mixture of light that is "transmitted" to the human eye has been modified by the gem. The remaining mixture of wavelengths is "added up" by the brain to perceive a single color. This absorption of certain colors, or wavelengths, is called the "selective absorption of light." This selective absorption of light wavelengths is always consistent for an individual gemstone. It is this consistency to absorb specific wavelengths that causes our perception of the color change effect when viewing a gem under two different light sources.

Apart from the standard factors used to assess gemstones, the quality and value of a color change gem is judged by:

1. The strength of the color change seen.

2. The distinctiveness and attractiveness of its color under candescent light (i.e., sunlight).

3. The distinctiveness and attractiveness of its color under incandescent light (i.e., most artificial light).

Double refraction

This is an optical "doubling" effect possessed by some gemstones (e.g., Zircon). In these gems we see a twin image of features in the gem. While this effect lends optical depth to a gem like a mirror maze, drawing you in, it doesn't make a gem more brilliant. Double refraction has one very unusual side effect that greatly intrigued early man, and, indeed, today some people still find fascinating - pleochroism.

Iridescence

This is the rainbow-like color effect seen in some gems and is caused by cracks or structural layers breaking up light into spectral colors. Fire Agate is a gemstone that shows this phenomenon to good effect. When iridescence occurs in metallic hues (called schiller) in Labradorite, it is commonly called "labradorescence." In Pearls, the subtle iridescence present is called the "orient."

Play of Color

These are flashes of rainbow colors in Opal that change with the angle of observation. This should not be confused with "opalescence," which is the milky blue or pearly appearance of Opal caused by the reflection of light.

Pleochroism

Atoms in some gemstones are arranged in such a manner that light rays are split into two separate components. As these two rays possess slightly different colors, the effect to the eye is that different colors are seen from a gem when viewed from different angles. This body color property is known as "pleochroism."

When cutting most pleochroic gems (e.g., Kunzite), lapidaries try to minimize the pleochroism and maximize the single best color. Andalusite is the opposite, as cutters try to orient the gem to get a pleasing mix of oranges, chocolates, yellows and greens.

Many gemstones are pleochroic, but the two component colors seen by the eyes are so similar that the pleochroism is not particularly visible. Examples of weak to medium pleochroic gems are Ruby, Sapphire, Emerald and Chrysoberyl.

Due to their crystal structure, some gemstones do not possess pleochroism. This lack of pleochroism is extremely useful for species determination. For example, Ruby and Red Spinel share many similar characteristics and often the only way of distinguishing between the two are by pleochroic tests. Notable examples of non-pleochroic stones are Spinel, Garnet and Diamond.

Andalusite is an unusual gem that is cut to maximize its pleochroism

Silk

Especially desirable in Rubies and Sapphires, this is the reflection of fibrous inclusions or canals that cause a silky appearance creating a soft, uniform distribution of sparkling light.

Certain inclusions in Rubies can create a silky appearance that softly sparkles light

GEMSTONE FORMATION

Ceylon Padparadscha Color Sapphire is a gem that can be formed by magma crystallization

For millions of years, gemstones have formed beneath the surface of the earth in a variety of different environments.

Traditionally, gemstones fall into three rock classifications: Igneous (Magmatic), Metamorphic and Sedimentary. Igneous or Magmatic rocks crystallize from molten magma, lava or gases. Sedimentary rocks crystallize from hydrous solutions on or near the earth's surface, while Metamorphic rocks re-crystallize from existing minerals that have been subjected to great pressure and high temperatures.

Gemstone formation is generally classified into four processes:

1. Molten rock and associated fluids.

2. Environmental changes.

3. Surface water.

4. Formation in the earth's mantle.

While potentially confusing, it should be noted that some gemstone varieties are formed by more than one process.

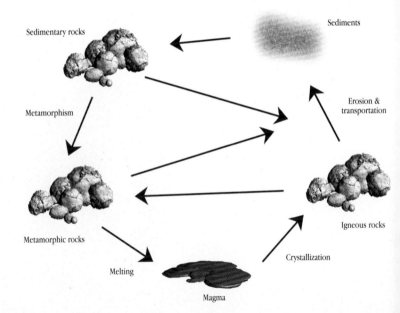

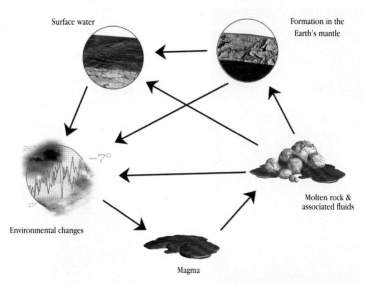

Surface water

Formation in the Earth's mantle

Environmental changes

Molten rock & associated fluids

Magma

Molten rock and associated fluids

Molten rock and associated fluids are minerals that are formed in the magma or its escaping fluids. They are created by heat deep within the earth. Molten rock and associated fluids are further classified into magma crystallization, gas crystallization, hydrothermal and pegmatites.

Magma crystallization

As magma cools, its various elements combine to form minerals. When one mineral forms, the available ingredients, temperature and pressure gradually change to create different minerals. While one mineral will occasionally crystallize, if the conditions are not suitable, no crystals will form and the magma will simply cool into aggregate rocks (i.e., solid masses of small, interlocking crystals).

Before all the magma can crystallize it will break into the crust and rush towards the earth's surface. When the pressure and temperature are too low for crystallization, the rest of the magma cools into fine-grained rocks with the original crystals distributed in

Magma crystallization

CRUST

MAGMA

GEMSTONE FORMATION

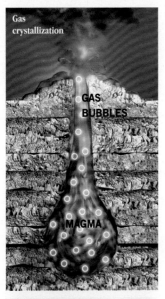

"phenocrysts" throughout the rocks' interiors. Gems formed in these conditions include Sapphire, Ruby, Moonstone, Garnet and Zircon.

Gas crystallization

While some gems grow on a solid base, others form inside gas bubbles. Gas bubbles are formed during a volcanic eruption when rising magma undergoes a rapid reduction in pressure. These bubbles often contain high concentrations of certain elements and with the right combination of temperature and pressure, gems including Garnet, Topaz and Spinel are formed.

Mozambique Garnet is a gem that can be formed by gas crystallization

Hydrothermal

Hydrothermal liquids are created when water and heat interact with magma deep inside the earth. These liquids contain water, carbon dioxide, special elements (such as fluorine and beryllium) and volatiles (substances that are readily vaporized) that have escaped from the magma through fractures and fissures. Hydrothermal liquids may dissolve minerals or combine with ground water as they solidify and form mineral veins. If combined with the right temperature, pressure, time and physical space, gems including Amethyst, Topaz and Emerald are formed.

Pegmatites

When magma in the upper part of the mantle becomes concentrated with volatiles it cools into a cavity called a pegmatite. As the molten rock begins to solidify, the elements begin to crystallize into gems including

Topaz, Tourmaline, Kunzite, Aquamarine and Morganite.

GEMSTONE FORMATION

Environmental changes

Environmental changes, such as changes in temperature or pressure, can alter existing minerals into something new. This process is called metamorphism and it is divided into two types, contact metamorphism and regional metamorphism.

1. **Contact metamorphism:** Contact metamorphism occurs when magma forces its way into an existing rock. The intense heat melts these rocks and re-crystallizes new minerals that are stable at higher temperatures. Gemstones formed by contact metamorphism include Garnet, Diopside, Spinel and Lapis Lazuli.

2. **Regional metamorphism:** The earth is composed of continental plates that float on the mantle. As some of them compete for the same space, their interaction is responsible for the formation of geographic features such as mountains. The intense heat and pressure generated by these geological events can cause minerals to become unstable, changing them into new varieties over time. Polymorphs are gemstones that re-crystallize into a new crystal system during regional metamorphism. Examples include Andalusite, Kyanite, Sillimanite, Tanzanite and some varieties of Garnet. In contrast, pseudomorphs like Tiger's Eye change their chemistry through atom-by-atom replacement during regional metamorphism.

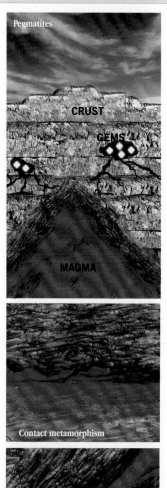

Siberian Emerald is a gem that can be formed by hydrothermal liquids

GEMSTONE FORMATION

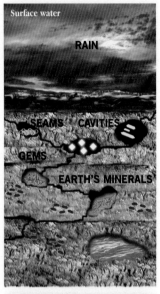

Surface water

Rain plays an important role in recycling minerals and creating new gems. As water passes through the earth, it picks up various chemicals that can react with each other in a variety of ways. When a dry season occurs after a period of heavy rainfall, water tables fall, leaving behind deposits of different minerals in seams and cavities. Depending on what chemicals the water has reacted with, gemstones including Opal, Turquoise, Malachite, Amethyst, Agate and Azurite are created.

African Fire Opal is a gem that can be formed by surface water

Gems formed in the earth's mantle

The earth's mantle is composed of molten rock and gases called magma. It is 83% of the earth's volume and 1,864 miles thick. Near the center, the mantle is extremely hot and kept in constant motion due to currents of heat. Where the mantle and crust meet, a tumultuous zone of high pressure and temperature is created.

Peridot and Diamond are examples of gemstones that crystallize at extremely high temperatures. Peridot deposits in Arizona were created on rocks floating in the mantle, approximately 20 to 55 miles below the earth's surface. Diamonds crystallize in the magma 109 to 149 miles below the earth's surface where the temperatures are higher and the magma is very fluid.

"The glowing Ruby should adorn those who in warm July are born, then will they be exempt and free from love's doubt and anxiety."

Unknown Author

MINING GEMSTONES

A baobab forest on the road to Ilakaka. Ilakaka is one of Madagascar's most prolific gem fields

Traditional gem mining techniques, such as this windlass, are still extensively used

Washing alluvial gem gravels in Ilakaka, Madagascar

In antiquity, most gemstones were discovered near the surface, generally by accident. While this has somewhat changed in modern times, prospecting for colored gemstones is still a fairly primitive affair, relying more on observation and chance, than the intensive scientific methods employed by the large multinational corporations involved in Diamond exploration. Once work begins on a gemstone deposit, it is correctly called a "mine."

One of the most intriguing aspects of gemstone mining is the diversity of techniques employed in their extraction. These range from low tech tools such as shovels and sieves, to the high tech methods used to extract Diamonds from pipes (i.e., a volcanic pathway that connects the earth's deep mantle to the surface). Apart from the introduction of power tools and pumps, most colored gem mining hasn't changed dramatically in thousands of years and still relies on three key things - perseverance, hand tools and elbow grease.

With a radiocarbon age of 43,000 years, the oldest known mine is the "Lion Cave" in Swaziland. At this site, people mined the iron-containing mineral Hematite, which they presumably ground to produce the red pigment, ochre. Sites of a similar age were also found by archaeologists in the Netherlands and Hungary, which may have been worked for flint in weapons and tools. Another early mining operation was the Turquoise mine operated by the ancient Egyptians at Wady Maghareh on the Sinai Peninsula. Turquoise was also mined in pre-Columbian America in the Cerillos mining district in New Mexico, where a mass of rock 197 feet in depth and 295 feet in width was removed with stone tools. The resulting mine dump of unusable rock covers 20 acres.

Gemstones are generally obtained by alluvial or host rock mining.

Alluvial mining

By far the most common method of mining gemstones, alluvial mining is the extraction of gems from sedimentary deposits, also known as placer or secondary deposits.

They are called secondary deposits because the gems are not found in the rock (i.e., host rock) in which they formed or are hosted, but in deposits caused by the weathering and erosion of primary deposits. It includes the prospecting of riverbeds (i.e., the water flow is dammed so the less dense clay and sand is swept away - the remaining gem gravel is then agitated so the gems can be extracted and sorted) or the mining of gems from sedimentary deposits located beneath the earth's surface (i.e., the digging of pits, vertical shafts and tunnels to reach gem gravels). A variation of alluvial mining is "marine mining," which is the mining of sandy coastal strata by dredging (e.g., Amber from Kaliningrad, Russia). Other examples of alluvial mining include river mining in Rathnapura, Sri Lanka and shaft mining in Ilakaka, Madagascar.

Typically, a miner will dig using either hand tools (on a small scale mine) or heavy industrial machinery. The earth is then taken to be washed either by hand or with the aid of machinery. This is exactly how it sounds - the loose earth is washed with water to get rid of the debris, leaving gemstones in the "wash." This wash is then trawled through to find the rough gemstones. It is an incredibly laborious and time consuming process that can from day to day, yield very little. Typically, only a few little gems remain at the end of washing and sorting.

Alluvial deposits tend to include more than one gem type and this can be useful, as the presence of one gem type can often indicate the presence of another. Such gems are called "tracer" gems, as they allow prospectors to "trace down" other varieties. Other methods of prospecting include the mapping of ancient riverbeds and streams.

Although gem crystals from alluvial deposits tend to be rounded, scratched and cracked due to the weathering processes they have endured, this is actually beneficial as the culling of poorer specimens has already occurred. In fact, the percentage of gem quality crystals found in alluvial deposits is generally higher than those obtained from primary host rock deposits.

Host rock mining

Also known as primary deposits, host rock mining is the chipping of gems from the rock in which they formed or are hosted. Crystals from these deposits are extracted from their host rock by hand tools, pneumatic tools and even explosives. Performed for centuries, this mining is typically done by digging underground tunnels. In some cases, gemstones can be harvested directly from underground caves, for example, the mining of Moonstone from limestone caves near the village of Kangayam in Tamil Nadu, southern India.

A lot of work for a little beauty, a day's yield from a Sapphire mine in Ilakaka, Madagascar

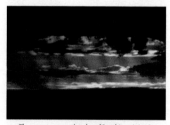

The sun sets on another day of Sapphire mining in Ilakaka, Madagascar

The author at the business end of a gem mine

MINING GEMSTONES

Garnet crystals still embedded in their host rock

Jim Fiebig, a regular special guest on GemsTV, drawing a crowd at a mining village in Madagascar

Mechanized gem washers in action at Brad Mitchell's mine in Songea, Tanzania

Depending on the hardness of the primary material, host rock mining can either be comparatively easy (e.g., mining of Kunzite from pegmatites at Betafo, Madagascar) or extremely difficult (e.g., mining of Tanzanite from metamorphic rocks at the Merelani Foothills in northern Tanzania).

While some gems are easily removed by picks or drills, sometimes the host material must be crushed before the gems can be extracted and sorted for quality. At the Cullinan mine in Pretoria, South Africa they use a "sticky table," which is a table covered in grease that the Diamond-rich Kimberlite (i.e., the host rock in which most Diamonds are found) stick to because of their density (i.e., the Kimberlite that contains no Diamonds falls away).

Ethical mining

GemsTV strongly encourages mining methods that are environmentally sound, such as:

1. Mining that protects streams, watersheds and ground water from pollutants, including silt, debris, rubbish and chemical/biological contaminants.

2. Mining that minimizes the destruction of plants, wildlife and habitat.

3. Reclaiming and replanting land after mining to restore it as closely as possible to its original condition.

For example, in the Masuguru district of Songea in southern Tanzania, one mine owner, Brad Mitchell, suffers from freelance miners encroaching on his holding. They destroy trees and excavate dozens of holes every day in search of the coveted Songea Sapphire. As it is a condition of his mining license that he leaves the area exactly as he found it, Brad ensures every hole is filled, more trees are planted than are removed and that the landscape is left in a better condition than when he arrived. Many countries ensure conditions such as these are adhered to; sadly, some do not.

GemsTV also strongly encourages fair labor practices that conform to local labor laws where our gems are mined or cut. We sell gems that have been mined using legitimate labor that has been paid a fair wage (i.e., no child labor, slave labor or unfair labor practices). Also, we believe mining and cutting facilities should provide a clean, safe and well lit working environment. For example, on August 10, 2006, the Thai Ministry of Labor recorded an average of only 0.62 milligrams of dust per cubic meter during the annual health and safety inspection of our workshops in Chanthaburi, Thailand - 15 milligrams per cubic meter is considered normal.

GEMSTONE CUTTING

Slicing

Pre-forming

Shaping

Polishing

Cutting (also know as Lapidary) is the process whereby a rough stone is turned into a gemstone. The process makes a gem assume a certain shape, bringing out its luster and color, enabling it to be set into jewelry.

Unlike Diamonds, colored gems possess variable optical properties and are not cut to a uniform ideal. A well-cut colored gem exhibits even color, an acceptable number of inclusions, good brilliance and shows the majority of carat weight when viewed from the top. Broadly, the styles of gem cutting can be divided into faceted gems (gems with geometrically shaped flat polished faces) and non-faceted gems (those gems that do not have geometrically shaped flat polished faces such as cabochons). The steps in faceting gemstones are:

1. **Slicing:** Also called cutting, slicing is one of the most crucial stages in the finishing of gemstones (if not the most crucial), as it will ultimately determine the size and beauty of the finished gem. Once the rough is selected, using a Diamond-tipped circular steel saw, the gem slicer will determine how to cut, where to cut, and how many pieces to cut, in order to produce the highest quality. If the rough is cut incorrectly its beauty may be diminished, relegating an exceptional gem to the ordinary.

2. **Pre-forming:** Once the rough has been carefully cut, pre-forming commences. This process requires tremendous experience and concentration. Pre-formers carry a great responsibility, as they must determine the most suitable shape for each gemstone. Apart from beauty, pre-formers always bear in mind the weight of the finished gem. Pre-forming is typically performed by using a vertical steel grinding wheel.

3. **Shaping:** The shaper uses a special type of heat activated resin to affix the pre-formed gemstone onto a metal rod, commonly called a "dob stick." The shaper then delicately applies the gemstone to the shaping wheel to obtain a more accurate presentation of the facets and size. Due to the immense precision required by this process, the shaper is usually a very experienced pre-former. Shaping is completed using a hand-operated shaping wheel.

4. **Polishing:** The final step is known as polishing. Once gemstones have reached their ideal size and shape, they are taken to a steel (or steel and

copper) horizontal polishing wheel where the polisher completes the faceting and gives them a final polish using fine Diamond paste to reveal their hidden luster, brilliance and fire.

The cut of a gemstone largely depends on the shape of the gem rough (i.e., the shape of the raw gem as it comes from the earth). The Oval cut is most frequently used, as it best balances beauty and carat weight retention. Factors to consider when choosing to facet a gem in another shape include design aesthetics, inclusions, carat weight loss and color. Gem cutters are considered "experts" once they have 2 years of experience and on average can facet 30 gems per day.

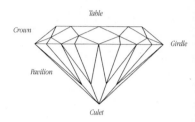

Stylized diagram showing the parts of a gemstone

Round brilliant cut

Round is from the Middle English word "rounden," which means "secret." The Round Brilliant cut is also known as the Round cut, American Ideal cut or American Standard cut.

The standard number of facets of a Round Brilliant cut gemstone is 57. Although no single inventor has officially been credited with the invention of the Round Brilliant cut, many sources do credit a Venetian cutter named Vincenzio Perruzzi and date the Brilliant's introduction to the 18th century.

The Russian mathematical genius Marcel Tolkowsky, a member of a large and powerful Diamond family, subsequently calculated the cuts necessary to create the ideal Diamond shape. As part of his PhD thesis in mathematics, Tolkowsky considered variables such as the index of refraction and covalent bond angles to describe what has become known as the Round Brilliant cut. Tolkowsky's recommended cut height for a Round Brilliant is 57.6% that of the diameter of the Diamond, which breaks down to about 43% for the pavilion, and 16% for the height of the crown. This 57.6% is probably the most crucial dimension of the gem. This cut is optically the most efficient. The Round Brilliant boasts one of the best recoveries for well shaped Diamond and gemstone rough; this translates into good value for consumers.

Round Brilliant Cut

The Round Brilliant cut is designed to provide maximum optics for brilliance and scintillation, making the gem sparkle and dance in the light. This cut was specially developed for Diamonds but is today common for all gem types.

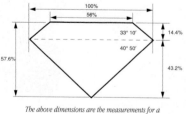

The above dimensions are the measurements for a Round Brilliant Cut Diamond

GEMSTONE CUTTING

Oval cut

Oval is from the Latin word "ovum" meaning "egg." The standard number of facets of an Oval cut gemstone is 69 and it has an elliptical shape when viewed from the top.

For the Oval cut, the ratio of the length to the width should be approximately 2:1, although this does vary slightly depending on the optical properties of different gem types. A well cut Oval gemstone can be nearly as bright as a Round Brilliant cut.

The Oval cut is a particularly beautiful shape and if well proportioned gives great scintillation and fire.

Oval Cut

Baguette cut

While Baguette is from the Italian word "bacchetta," meaning "rod or stick," to the Native American Navajo, the oblong symbolizes the female form, intelligence and divine contemplation.

The Baguette shaped gemstone is really only a special oblong shape and approximately 20 facets. Most oblong cuts are "step" cut, which means that the facets on the pavilion have been cut in steps, parallel to the edges, in the manner of a pyramid with its top chopped off. The base and table are square with triangular facets.

The Baguette cut best suits gem types whose rough crystals occur in a similar shape (e.g., Tourmaline).

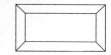

Baguette Cut

Square cut

Square is from the Vulgar Latin word "exquadra," meaning "square shape."

The standard number of facets of a Square cut gemstone is 57 and is really only a special oblong shape where the sides are the same length. Most oblong cuts are "step" cut, which means that the facets on the pavilion have been cut in steps, parallel to the edges, in the manner of a pyramid with its top chopped off.

Some believe this cut is a symbol for equality, fair mindedness, justice, order, satisfaction and truth.

Square Cut

Trilliant cut

The standard number of facets of a Trilliant cut gemstone is 43. Trilliant cut gemstones are based on a triangular shape. Usually with truncated corners and

GEMSTONE CUTTING

Trilliant Cut

Pear Cut

displaying a variety of facet designs, this cut creates a spectacular wedge of brilliant fire. The tips and culets of Trilliants are pointed and thin. As a result, some jewelers only bezel-set Trilliants, even though prongs that protect the tips work well and show more of the gem.

As you look down through the gem, the culet generally appears centered in the middle of the table showing the pavilion of the gem with an attention to symmetry. When you examine the gem in profile, the girdle and table facet are generally parallel. The pavilion's main facet usually extends from the culet perpendicularly until it intersects the girdle. Because of their equilateral form, Trilliants return lots of light and color. They are considered nearly as brilliant as Round cuts, so they are a great choice for customers who like brilliance, but want something other than round. Variations include rounded-corner triangles, modified shield cuts and triangular step cuts.

There should be as few polishing marks as possible and the surface should appear glossy and reflective. Good polishing helps maximize brilliance and scintillation in Trilliants.

Trilliants work well with light-colored gems - such as Diamonds, Aquamarines, Beryls and White Sapphires - where cutters try to maximize brilliance. Inversely, some cutters use Trilliants to effectively lighten and brighten the appearance of darker gems such as Tanzanite, Spessartite Garnet, Rhodolite Garnet and Amethyst.

First developed in Amsterdam, the exact design can vary depending on a particular gem's natural characteristics and the cutter's personal preferences. It may be a traditional triangular shape with pointed corners or a more rounded triangular shape with 25 facets on the crown, 19 facets on the pavilion and a polished girdle. Some twinned Diamond rough (a crystal growing within a crystal) is naturally triangular (called "Macle") and is ideal for Trilliants.

Pear cut

The standard number of facets of a Pear cut gemstone is 71. A hybrid cut, combining the best of the Oval and the Marquise, it is shaped like a sparkling teardrop. A nice Pear cut is generally one that is well cut with a polished girdle.

Although it varies depending on the optical properties of each gem type, Pear cuts should generally have a good depth such as 1.5:1 aspect ratio for a great look and a lively gem. For rings, this cut compliments a hand with small or average length fingers. It is particularly beautiful for pendants and earrings.

While color shows fairly dramatically in a Pear cut gemstone, the world's largest cut Diamond (the Cullinan I mounted in the British Royal Scepter) is a Pear cut.

Octagon cut

The standard number of facets of an Octagon cut gemstone is 53. This is another "step" cut but with the four corners mitered. The facets run in steps parallel to the gemstone circumference. This cut is differentiated from the Emerald cut by steps on the pavilion that are not equidistant.

With this cut, color plays a very important role in the beauty of the gemstone as color tends to show very dramatically in Octagon cut gemstones.

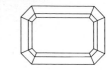

Octagon Cut

Emerald cut

The approximate number of facets of an Emerald cut gemstone is 50. The Emerald cut looks like a rectangle from the top, with truncated corners. These can be beautiful gemstones with stepped facets; the sheen tends to display large flashes of these stepped angles on the pavilion of the gem.

This is another "step" cut and it has rows of facets that resemble a staircase and usually are four-sided or elongated. It is known as a step cut because its concentric, broad, flat planes resemble stair steps.

The Emerald cut is differentiated from the Octagon cut by its equidistant steps on the pavilion. The flat planes of the outside edges allow for a variety of shapes. Generally, the length-to-width ratio should be 1.5:1 to 1.75:1.

With this cut, color plays a very important role in the beauty of the gemstone as color tends to show very dramatically in Emerald cut gemstones. The Emerald cut was developed specifically for Emeralds to reduce the amount of pressure exerted during cutting and to protect the gemstone from chipping. Today, modern cutting techniques make this less important and it is used for a wide variety of gem types.

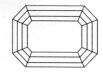

Emerald Cut

GEMSTONE CUTTING

Marquise cut

The standard number of facets of a Marquise cut gemstone is 57. The Marquise cut is also known as the "Navette" shape and looks like a long oval that has been stretched out to a point at each end like a football viewed straight down from the top.

The general ratio of length to width should be 2:1. It is important that the Marquise-cut gem not be too shallow or light will pass through the back of the gem diminishing its brilliance and color. However, as with all colored gems, this can vary from type to type.

Marquise cut provides good brilliance and color and is gorgeous when used as a solitaire or when enhanced by smaller gems.

The Marquise cut was inspired by the fetching smile of the Marquise de Pompadour and commissioned by the Sun King, France's Louis XIV, who wanted a Diamond to match the smile.

Marquise Cut

Antique cushion cut

Antique is from the Latin word "antiquis," meaning "classic" and is a primary cut first used on Ruby and Sapphire faceted in Sri Lanka.

The approximate number of facets of an Antique Cushion cut gemstone is 64 and is also known as "The Old Miner" or "Old European" cut, because it looks like a cross between a deep cut with large facets that was common in the late 19th and the early 20th centuries and a modern Oval cut. As it looks somewhat like a sofa cushion, the word "Cushion" is typically used in combination with "Antique," but generally only when the sides are equidistant.

This shape is also sometimes referred to as the "Pillow" cut (for obvious reasons) or the "Candlelight" cut in reference to cuts designed prior to electric lights, when gems sparkled in the light provided by candles. It has a marvelously romantic and classic look that stands out from other cuts and along with the Princess cut, the Antique Cushion cut maximizes a gem's luster.

Antique Cushion Cut

Princess cut

Technically known as "Square Modified Brilliant" cut, the Princess cut is a square version of the Round Brilliant cut with 76 sparkling facets.

Depth percentages of 70% to 78% are not uncommon

in the Princess cut and it is a "Brilliant Style" shape with sharp, uncut corners (i.e., "Brilliant Style" refers to the vertical direction of the crown and pavilion facets).

It is a relatively new cut and often finds its way into solitaire engagement rings. Flattering to a hand with long fingers, it is often embellished with triangular stones at its sides. Because of its design, this cut requires more weight to be directed toward the gem's depth in order to maximize brilliance. The advantages of the Princess cut are not restricted purely to Diamonds; it is also used on many other gemstones. Because of the extra faceting, and the effects this produces, Princess cuts are naturally more brilliant and sparkly.

The Princess cut generally works best with lighter colored transparent gemstones and along with the Antique Cushion cut, the Princess cut maximizes a gem's luster.

The Princess cut was designed for weight retention of octahedral Diamond crystals, helping to create more attractive Diamonds at more reasonable prices. The Barion cut was the forerunner of the Princess cut and was invented about 30 years ago by Basil Watermeyer of Johannesburg. The Barion cut has been the subject of patents that have expired within the past ten years and this has led to the greater availability of similarly cut gemstones. The style we now know as the "Princess" cut has since become a generic style of cutting. According to Harold Newman's "Illustrated Dictionary of Jewelry," the term "Princess" cut was previously applied to what is now known as the "Profile" cut developed by Arpad Nagy of London in 1961.

Princess Cut

Heart shape cut

The standard number of facets of a Heart Shape cut gemstone is 59 and is a pear-shaped gemstone or Diamond with a cleft at the top. Generally, a Heart Shape's length to width ratio is slightly over 1:1, approximately 1.1:1 in favor of length, but usually not over 1.2:1.

The ultimate symbol of love, most Heart Shape cut gems are nearly round. This has the advantage of having a nearly round pavilion that provides beautiful brilliance. Most Heart Shape cuts are purchased as single gems. Solitaire rings are set with hearts throughout the range of sizes. After necklaces and

Heart Shape Cut

GEMSTONE CUTTING

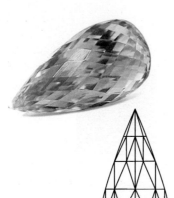

Briolette Cut

Fancy cut Rhodolite Garnets

rings, most Heart Shape cuts are sold as matched pairs for stud earrings. The primary market for Hearts is for luxury jewelry and there is heavy interest in the Heart Shape cut in the Far East.

Hearts must be extremely well cut which makes them more expensive because excellent proportions result from a greater expenditure of rough. Understandably, noticeable increases in sales of Heart Shape cut gems occur around Valentine's Day. As with all fancy cuts, buyers of Hearts should look first at the overall make. The first question to ask is, "Do I find the gem pleasing to the eye?" Generally, look for a balanced shape, avoiding extremes. Lobes should be rounded, and the cleft should be relatively sharp and distinct.

Briolette cut

The Briolette cut is believed to derive its name from the French words "Brilliant" (brilliant or sparkling) and "Brignolette" (a small dried plum).

The Briolette cut is a drop or pear-shaped gemstone with shaped facets all the way around. There is no table, crown or pavilion. Considering the shape of the Briolette, it is the most difficult to cut and an experienced cutter can only cut and polish 5-10 Briolette gemstones per day. Because of the specific number of cuts to show the facets, the Briolette cut requires perfection from top to bottom. While the approximate number of facets of a Briolette cut gemstone is 84, the more facets the drop has, the more brilliant it is.

The Briolette is a type of Rose cut, which dates back to the 14th century or earlier. No one knows for certain how old the Briolette cut actually is. There are rumors of Diamonds cut in India during the 12th century exhibiting this style of cutting. The Briolette is a relatively rare Diamond cut and far more common for colored gemstones. Most Diamond Briolettes are cut from white rough, but colored Diamond Briolettes, especially Fancy and Canary Yellows, are becoming more popular, followed by Cognacs and Champagnes.

Briolette gems are found in antique tiaras and estate jewelry from the Victorian, Edwardian and Art Deco eras. Today, Briolette gems are increasing popular in fashion jewelry. Briolette cuts are primarily set in earrings, necklaces and pendants. They are often used for earrings with a hanging wire or a simple precious metal cap, sometimes with a small Diamond accent.

Briolettes have been featured in many industry publications and also in Vogue and Harper's Bazaar. Every Briolette is unique, so look for beauty and lots of brilliance.

Fancy cut

For those who want something really different, recent advances in cutting technology have produced a breathtaking range of innovative new shapes such as flowers, clover leaves, stars, triangles, kites and all manner of fancy cuts.

Some of the new designs are variations on standard shapes, aimed at creating the illusion of a bigger, more perfect gemstone. Others play with the natural rough and still others are fashioned into revolutionary new shapes.

The important fact to remember is that this ever-widening choice of shapes and designs is being created to suit a variety of individual styles and tastes. No one cut is more beautiful than another. The magic of nature and the artistry of the cutter combine to make each a unique work of art.

Cabochon cut

The word Cabochon is derived from the old Norman French word "caboche," meaning head.

A Cabochon is a polished gemstone with a flat bottom (or slightly rounded bottom) and a convex or rounded domed top. The traditional Cabochon is an Oval but Cabochons can also be fashioned into other shapes including Triangles and Rectangles.

Cabochons, commonly known as Cabs, are the oldest and most common form of gem cutting. Gems cut "en Cabochon" are shaped and polished, rather than cut. In antiquity, this was generally the only cutting option available other than using the gem with the natural facets of their crystal structure. Some of the most beautiful ancient jewelry was made with Cabochons, including astounding Royal East Indian jewelry and the breastplate of Aaron.

Cabochons are used for making jewelry, often carved as intaglio or cameo, and are also used in crystal healing. Today, the Cabochon cut is applied to gems of limited transparency (e.g., Turquoise, Jade, Agate, etc.) or as a result of predominant inclusions (e.g., relatively opaque Sapphires, Rubies or Emeralds) or for gems where the cut's curved surface accentuates

Cabochon Cut

Popular since antiquity, cameos are a style of cutting that clearly demonstrates the art behind gem cutting

GEMSTONE CUTTING

special characteristics (e.g., iridescence, chatoyancy or the cat's eye effect, asterism or the star effect, etc.).

Buff top cut

A Cabochon variant for transparent gems, the Buff Top cut mixes a faceted cut with a non-faceted cut. This results in a gem with the typical domed top of a Cabochon and a faceted pavilion, giving the illusion of depth as the eye is drawn into the center of the gem. The cut shows good brilliance and has a crown that is less easily abraded than those of faceted gems.

Buff Top Cut

Millennium cut

Possessing an incredible 1,000 facets, the Millennium cut is so named as it was created by Rogerio Graca around 1999 as a unique and challenging symbol of the new millennium.

While sometimes confused with the Concave cut, the Millennium cut is easy to spot as it creates a gem packed full of facets.

One Millennium cut gem equates to approximately 18 times the amount of work of other cuts. Having 624 facets on the pavilion and 376 facets on the table, each facet has to be touched from one to four times during cutting and polishing.

The amount of time involved, combined with the design particularities (rough selection, keeping a degree of sharpness between each facet, making enough space for each facet, etc.) and the need for precision machinery, eliminates the possibility of the Millennium cut ever becoming mainstream.

Mirror Cut

Concave cut

The Concave cut is a three dimensional conical shaped facet applied to the pavilion of the gem that creates depth as well as length and breadth. Instead of the facets being joined by an angle they are joined with a groove. This third dimension allows the gem to refract more light, thereby maximizing its brilliance. The Concave cut also distributes light more evenly, giving the gem a homogeneous interior glow.

While it is sometimes confused with the Millennium cut it can be easily distinguished by the lack of a standard number of facets and its application only to the pavilion.

Concave Cut

While Doug Hoffman patented Concave cut technology in the early nineties, his friend Richard Homer is credited as perfecting the technique of the Concave cut. While working towards a Geology Degree, Homer began cutting gems in 1974 to help pay his tuition. Since then, his designs have won 15 American Gem Trade Association (AGTA) Cutting Edge Awards.

Not all gems benefit from the Concave cut. Optimizing color and light is always the first consideration in cutting gems, and although Diamonds and lighter-toned gems increase up to 100% in brilliance when Concave cut, darker gems like Rubies can appear murkier and less attractive. Furthermore, the Concave cut is more expensive than traditionally cut gems, due to the higher weight loss and the additional labor required.

Mirror cut

The Mirror cut is characterized by an extraordinarily large table and thick girdle consisting of as much as 90% of the width of the gem. This makes the gem highly refractive and literally gives it the properties of a mirror, hence the name.

Sometimes referred to as the "Thin Stone," the Mirror cut was an early 16th century phenomenon that is making a comeback. It is a variety of the Round cut and appears in the names of some historic Diamonds including the "Mirror of Portugal" and the "Mirror of France."

GEMSTONE TREATMENTS

Skillfully merging art and science, a variety of techniques are used to help gemstones reach their full potential. As critical as good cutting, enhancements and treatments are an integral part of the modern gemstone industry. With its roots in antiquity (e.g., heat treatment has been practiced in India for over 4,000 years), most of the techniques used simply facilitate the beautiful end results of the earth's natural processes. Below are some answers to common gemstone enhancement, treatment and care questions.

Is the use of enhancements and treatments globally accepted?

With close to 99% of the more popular gem types enhanced, as long as they are disclosed, all permanent enhancements and treatments are globally accepted. As the majority of gemstones traded internationally have undergone some form of enhancement, always assume treatments when purchasing gemstones.

Are all enhancements and treatments permanent?

With the exception of Emeralds, whose beauty is enhanced by the application of oils or polymers, GemsTV only knowingly accepts enhancements and treatments that are permanent with normal wear. Our information sources for gem enhancements and treatments include university mineralogical, gemological and geology departments, gem laboratories, trade associations, regulatory bodies, professional journals, books, the internet, and individual experts.

Do enhancements or treatments affect a gem's value?

For some varieties there is no difference between the values of enhanced, treated or natural gemstones. However, high quality unheated Rubies and Sapphires are extremely rare and command a much higher market price. When attempting to purchase Rubies and Sapphires, please be aware that unheated/untreated specimens are almost non-existent, and as a result, always purchase from a reliable supplier or have the seller's claim verified by a gemologist.

Tanzanite is a gemstone that would not be available in commercial quantities if it wasn't heat treated

How do I care for my gemstone jewelry?

Caring for your gemstone jewelry (i.e., normal wear) is a matter of common sense and simple precaution. For gemstone specific care instructions, please refer to the table below.

- Always remove your jewelry when engaging in activities that risk impact or exposure to chemicals or heat such as sports or housework.
- Always put jewelry on after using cosmetics, hair spray or perfumes, not before.
- Never remove your jewelry by pulling on the gems.
- Never store your jewelry in heaps and always store your gem necklaces flat. The best way to store your gemstone jewelry is in the separate compartments of a jewelry box or in cloth pouches.
- Carefully wipe jewelry with a soft lint-free cloth after each wearing to remove oils and salts.
- Once in a while, take the time to clean your jewelry. Always clean your jewelry with a cleaning solution or mechanical cleaner suitable for the gem.

What are mechanical cleaners?

The most common mechanical cleaners are ultrasonic and steam cleaners. Ultrasonic cleaners feature two basic parts: a small motor and a cleaning tank. The machine's motor produces ultrasonic energy that is transmitted with vibrating energy waves (usually 40,000 sound waves per second) to create microscopic bubbles in the cleaning tank. Called cavitation, this motion knocks dirt off the jewelry and is very effective in penetrating the tiny crevices in jewelry that traditional cleaning cloths and topical cleaners cannot easily reach. A steam cleaner uses jets of steam to literally blast dirt off jewelry. As some gemstones can be damaged by mechanical cleaners, always check to see if your gemstone is suitable.

How are gemstones enhanced or treated?

The following pages show the enhancements and treatments used for some popular gemstones, their purpose, frequency and care. For information on other gemstone varieties, please visit www.GemsTV.com.

GEMSTONE TREATMENTS

Are all gemstones treated?

No, the following list includes gemstones that are not treated.

Agate (Dendritic, Fire, Iris & Moss)	Manganotantalite
	Marcasite
Ambyglonite	Mawsitsit
Anatase	Mellite
Andalusite	Milarte
Andesine	Moldavite
Anglesite	Monazite
Apophyllite	Montebrasite
Aragonite	Mookite
Axinite	Moonstone
Azurite (Druzy)	Natrolite
Barite	Nephrite (Cat's Eye)
Bastnaesite	Nuummit
Bloodstone	Obsidian
Boracite	Oligoclase
Brazilianite	Opal (Fire & Moss)
Burbankite	Parisite
Bustamite	Pectolite
Calcite	Petalite
Cassiterite	Pezzottaite
Celestite	Phenakite
Charoite	Pollucite
Chrysoberyl (Brown, Green, Yellow)	Prehnite
	Pyrite
Chrysoprase	Pyroxmangite
Cinnabar	Quartz (Cat's Eye, Rutilated & Rose)
Clinohumite	
Creedite	Remondite
Danburite (White)	Rhodochrosite
Datolite	Scapolite (Yellow)
Diopside	Scapolite (Violet)
Dolomite	Scheelite
Dumortierite	Scolecite
Ekanite	Sellaite
Enstatite	Senarmontite
Eosphorite	Serandite
Epidote	Shortite
Euclase	Siderite
Eudialyte	Sillimanite
Fire Beryl?	Sinhalite
Fluorite (White)	Smithsonite
Fossils	Sphalerite
Gahnite	Sphene
Garnet	Spinel
Genthelvite	Staurolite
Glacier Topaz?	Sugilite
Hauyne	Sunstone
Heliodor (Cat's Eye)	Tanolite?
Hematite	Thaumasite
Hemimorphite	Tourmaline (some varieties)
Herderite	Tremolite
Howlite (White)	Tugtupite
Idocrase	Unakite
Iolite	Vesuvianite
Jasper (Multi Colored)	Villiaumite
Kornerupine	Wilsonite
Kunzite (Green & Cat's Eye)	Wulfenite
Kyanite	Zultanite
Larimar Leifite	
Magnesite	

GEMSTONE TREATMENTS

GEMSTONE	HARDNESS	TREATMENT	EXPLANATION	CARE	STEAM CLEANING	ULTRASONIC CLEANING
ALEXANDRITE	8.5	Colorless oils, wax and resins in fissures.	Used to improve appearance, these treatments are rarely used.	Normal care.	Yes.	No.
AMETHYST	7	Heated.	Used to lighten color and/or to remove smokiness, this treatment is only occasionally applied.	Normal care. Some gemstones fade or revert to their original color when exposed to strong light. Do not wear or leave them for extended periods under these conditions.	Yes.	No.
AQUAMARINE	7.5 - 8	Heated.	Used to remove yellow components to produce a purer blue color, this treatment is usually applied.	Normal care.	Yes.	No.
CITRINE	7	Heated or irradiated.	Usually applied, this treatment produces color.	Normal care. Some gemstones fade or revert to their original color when exposed to strong light. Do not wear or leave them for extended periods under these conditions.	Yes.	No.
DIAMOND (COLOR ENHANCED)	10	The process known as color enhancement involves using clean Diamonds and modifying their color with a combination of electron bombardment and heat, using safe electron-accelerator technology. This process exactly duplicates the natural exposure of Diamond crystals to radioactive elements during their formation.	Used to improve color intensity or to produce unique colors, this treatment is always applied.	Normal care.	Yes.	Yes.
EMERALD	7.5 - 8	Colorless oils, polymers, wax, resins in fissures, and/or dyed with the use of colored oils, and/or open fractures or cavities filled with hardened resins.	These treatments improve appearance. Colorless oils, polymers, wax, resins in fissures are usually applied. Dying with the use of colored oils is occasionally applied. Open fractures or cavities filled with hardened resins are commonly applied.	Normal care.	No.	No.
OPAL (BLACK, SEMI-BLACK & WHITE)	5.5 - 6	Impregnated with colorless oils, waxes, plastic or resins.	Used to improve durability, appearance and color, this treatment is rarely applied.	Normal care. Some gemstones are prone to crack due to loss of structural water. Keep away from heat and drying environments. Some gemstones are prone to damage due to thermal shock. Do not expose them to extreme temperature changes.	No.	No.

GEMSTONE TREATMENTS

GEMSTONE	HARDNESS	TREATMENT	EXPLANATION	CARE	STEAM CLEANING	ULTRASONIC CLEANING
PEARL (CULTURED)	2.5 - 4.5	Bleached, dyed or chemically treated.	Occasionally used, these treatments improve color and uniformity.	Clean either by wiping gently with a moist cloth or rinsing and gently patting dry with a soft cloth.	No.	No.
PERIDOT	6.5 - 7	Heat, colorless oil, wax or resins in fissures, and/ or filled fractures with colorless hardened resin.	Used to improve appearance, this treatment is rarely applied. Rarely heated to oxidize specific minerals to enhance color.	Normal care. Some gemstones are prone to damage due to thermal shock. Do not expose them to extreme temperature changes.	No.	No.
RUBY & SAPPHIRE	9	Heated and/or the healing of fissures and/or glass-filled open fractures and cavities, and/or lead glass-filled open fractures and cavities, and/or dyed and/or bulk diffusion of certain elements during the heating process, and/or colorless oil or resin in fissures.	Usually applied, these treatments produce, intensify or lighten color and/or improve color uniformity and/or appearance. Examples of the additives used include beryllium (i.e., light element) to permanently improve color and borax or lead (i.e., glass) to permanently improve appearance.	Normal care. Fillers in voids/cavities, fissures and/or open fractures can scratch more easily than the host gem or be more vulnerable to damage from heat or some chemicals.	Yes.	Yes.
TANZANITE	6.5 - 7	Heated.	Usually applied, this treatment produces the colors for which this gem is known.	Normal care. Some gemstones are prone to damage due to thermal shock. Do not expose them to extreme temperature changes.	No.	No.
TOPAZ (EXCEPT WHITE)	8	Irradiated, heated, coatings and/or diffused.	Used to improve color intensity or to produce unique colors, these treatments are usually applied. Physical Vapour Deposition (PVD) coating involves the application of a bonded layer of fine titanium atoms (US Patent Number 5,853,826 for Azotic Coating Technologies Inc.). When this oxide treatment falls within a certain thickness, optical interference produces a variety of colors.	Normal care. Some gemstones fade or revert to their original color when exposed to strong light. Do not wear or leave them for extended periods under these conditions. Gemstones with superficial color (or phenomena) surface layers are not suitable for re-cutting or re-polishing.	No.	No.
TOURMALINE	7 - 7.5	Heated and/or irradiated and/or filling of colorless oils, resins and waxes in fissures, and/or cavities/fractures filled with colorless hardened substances.	Used to improve color intensity and appearance these treatments are commonly applied.	Normal care.	Yes.	No.
ZIRCON (BLUE, RED, WHITE & YELLOW)	6.5 - 7	Heated.	Used to improve color this treatment is always applied.	Normal care. Some gemstones fade or revert to their original color when exposed to strong light. Do not wear or leave them for extended periods under these conditions.	Yes.	No.

THE GEM SUPPLY CHAIN

The colored gem industry supply chain is extremely long - far longer than the Diamond supply chain. It is not uncommon for a gemstone to pass through seven intermediaries from the mine to the consumer. By any industry standard, this is an extremely long and inefficient supply chain. Although the price keeps going up, other than at the cutting and setting stages, there is no real value being added to the gem.

On its passage through so many intermediaries, it is not uncommon for a colored gemstone to increase in price by up to 1,000%! For example, this means a $200 Tanzanite gemstone from Tanzania may end up selling for $2,000 in the jeweler's window and this does not even include the other jewelry components. Once you factor in labor, gold and Diamonds, our Tanzanite that started at $200 could end up retailing in a shop window for a whopping $4,000!

At GemsTV, our aim is to remove as many intermediaries as possible.

It is not uncommon for a gemstone to pass through seven intermediaries from the mine to the consumer

JEWELRY MAKING

The GemsTV jewelry workshop accommodates all aspects of both silver (925 Sterling) and gold (14K and 18K) handcrafted jewelry creation, including gem faceting, gem matching, design conceptualization, master model construction, wax injection, casting, jewelers (pre-finishing), gem setting, polishing and plating and quality assurance.

Gem cutting and gem matching

Completely reliant on the eyes and hands of skilled professionals, expert faceting and matching for size and color is critical in ensuring that the key ingredients in a gorgeous handcrafted piece of jewelry, the gems themselves, really shine! Before being set in jewelry, qualified professionals carefully examine each gem, separating them according to their clarity, color, cut and carat weight. With satisfaction as our highest priority, GemsTV invests tremendous effort towards ensuring that only the highest quality gems are perfectly matched before being set into a stunning array of handcrafted jewelry designs.

Sorting gemstones

Jewelry design

Jewelry design is both an art and surprisingly, a science. Inspiration and ideas come from the most unexpected sources. With a rich and varied color palette, using both hand-drawn and computer-aided design, our design team imagines stunning jewelry creations to complement our gemstones.

Designing jewelry

Our jewelry design team is led by Debby Cavill, Director of Merchandising. A British national, Debby is a jewelry industry veteran who transferred to our workshops in Chanthaburi, Thailand. She regularly travels the world's major jewelry markets in Asia, Europe and the US to stay abreast of the latest design and fashion trends. With Debby at the helm, GemsTV has the expertise and flexibility to design high quality contemporary jewelry that is current with the latest European, global and Hollywood fashions, as well as timeless pieces that embody classic design. Keeping you at the forefront of fashion, style and beauty, in November 2006 GemsTV was delighted to have one of our rings featured in British Vogue.

Working hand in hand with our master model makers and jewelers, our design team ensures that their creations are realized exactly how they were imagined.

The GemsTV Lemon Citrine 14K Yellow Gold Ring featured in the November, 2006 issue of British Vogue

JEWELRY MAKING

GemsTV has over 13,000 existing designs and creates over 70 new designs every day.

Handmade jewelry

For smaller quantities, the jeweler literally starts with an amount of gold and then cuts, shapes, heats and stretches it into the final jewelry. For larger quantities, we make an original masterpiece and then cast the required quantity of pieces from the master, finishing them all by hand.

A handmade ring starts to take form

Many of the handcrafted pieces start from gold bars or grains. The jewelers are given the correct amount for the design and then alloy is added to create 14K or 18K gold. The first step is to soften the gold to make it easier to craft. To do this, the jeweler uses an atmosphere control melter to heat the gold to a temperature of 1,877 °F.

For some designs, rather than starting with nuggets of gold, the jeweler starts with a length of gold that is already shaped into a round rod. The equipment we use to stretch the gold to the correct thickness is traditional and the skills have been passed on through many generations. Once the gold has been heated and cut into a rough state, the jeweler then starts to shape the body of the ring. This art is fascinating to watch, as within minutes you see a flat piece of gold transformed into jewelry by artisans whose only tools are their hammers and a wealth of experience.

Hand making jewelry

Master model construction

When handcrafting larger quantities, we use a wax molding technique to construct the first step of the ring. The master model making workshop comprises two sections - silver model makers and wax carvers. Their expertise is diverse and includes everything from simple prong set and lightweight gemstone jewelry designs to artistically crafted masterpieces. These craftspeople are of critical importance, as their ability to turn a one-dimensional drawing into a three-dimensional master model is vital in ensuring that the finished jewelry exceeds all expectations. As with the old carpenter's adage, measure twice cut once, all our master models must be exactingly precise, as any mistakes at this stage are going to appear in the finished jewelry.

Master model construction

Our designers, model makers and jewelry teams work closely together to ensure the very best results are achieved.

Wax injection

The wax injection department comprises four sections: rubber mold making, wax injection, quality control and repair and wax tree preparation. While the wax injection team carefully works with pre-set wax injection machines, the rubber mold makers understand the importance of correctly prepared rubber molds for improved wax injection. The quality control team ensures wax pieces are cleaned and in proper condition for casting.

While all this sounds very complicated, the handcrafting process is actually very simple. From a drawing we produce either a silver or wax master model. Once we have a master model, we make a mold of this using rubber. We then use these rubber molds to make multiple wax copies and these are then checked to ensure they are perfect. Remember, each of these will be a piece of handcrafted jewelry after casting - any mistakes here will show up in the finished design. Next, individual wax molds are affixed to a wax tree ready for casting.

Casting

At the GemsTV jewelry workshop, the casting room includes the complete array of equipment for handcrafting jewelry, including preparation facilities, curing ovens, vacuum casting, a high water pressure cleaning area and wastewater disposal facilities. With the right experts controlling this process, the very best results are achieved ensuring minimal complications for other processes later on. Again, like wax injection, the process itself is actually very simple. We simply put the tree of wax molds in a cylinder, pour in ceramic cement, heat up the cylinders until the wax melts out, pour in the gold or silver in a vacuum to ensure every crevice is filled, wait till the metal sets, crack and clean away the ceramic cement and our handcrafted jewelry is well on its way to taking shape.

Jewelers (pre-finishing)

Once removed from the casting tree, the pieces of jewelry, while starting to take shape, have a while to go before they look like the gorgeous handcrafted creations you see on GemsTV. Our jewelers carefully prepare and assemble the jewelry components ready for gem setting, all the while understanding the finishing needs for each individual design. In the case

JEWELRY MAKING

Checking wax molds for quality

Trees of wax molds ready for casting

Casting gold

JEWELRY MAKING

Pre-finishing a white gold ring

Gem setting takes a keen eye and a deft hand

The GemsTV gem setting department hard at work

of bracelet assembly, the components are all assembled by hand with the only high technology employed being laser welding for superior strength. As with all stages involved in handcrafting jewelry, an embedded quality control team approves every handcrafted piece before they are transferred to the next stage.

Gem setting

The gem setting team employs carefully selected gem-setters with abilities in both quality and quantity setting; true craftsmen and women, they handset an average of 150 gemstones per day per person. GemsTV has successfully produced a multitude of handcrafted jewelry designs featuring a wide variety of gemstones. Having a proven record with gemstone setting, GemsTV continuously ensures that the highest quality standards are met, while breaking new ground in both the types of setting and the gems within them.

Polishing and plating

At the polishing stage, we ensure that the best shine and finish are achieved but not at the expense of essential design details. This is done by carefully separating individual polishing needs. When plating is required, plating specialists apply a carefully calculated formula of rhodium or gold plating with an emphasis on both color and brightness.

Quality assurance

Quality assurance at the GemsTV jewelry workshop encompasses two areas. The first being quality control teams that check each step of the handcrafting process and secondly, the final quality assurance after polishing. The successful implementation of quality control teams has helped minimize and eliminate problems and plays a key role in maximizing the quality of our handcrafted jewelry. The final product approval is done by quality assurance professionals with years of experience in the creation of high quality handcrafted jewelry. By working closely with quality control teams embedded in each department, they ensure quality standards always exceed expectations. This method ensures that suggestions and improvements are easily implemented throughout the creation of our handcrafted jewelry, where and whenever required.

Corporate citizenship

JEWELRY MAKING

Employing over 1,700 people in Thailand, our working conditions are equal to or better than those of Western manufacturers. For those who have visited Thailand, you will know that it is the land of smiles. The smiles in our workshop are there for three good reasons: the working environment is of a high standard, the pay is good, and most importantly, the whole team is free to express themselves through the jewelry they create.

In cooperation with the Chanthaburi Polytechnic College we have launched an intensive jewelry course. Open to anyone between the ages of 18-25, we subsidize the tuition fees for graduates and guarantee all graduating students employment within our Company. Our Company supplies all materials and equipment. This intensive course is made all the more practical by our workshop leaders' and supervisors' regular guest lectures. Generating 50+ new employees every month, this program has proven very successful.

Thailand, the land of smiles

In cooperation with the Chanthaburi Polytechnic College we have launched an intensive jewelry course

JEWELRY SETTINGS

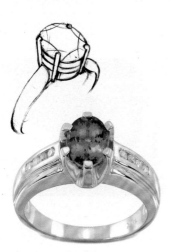

Prong Setting

Bezel Setting

Most jewelry is crafted from individual components. The pieces are often created on the jeweler's bench and then skillfully joined together. The components needed in most types of jewelry are incredibly simple. Even the most expensive "Tiffany-style" Diamond ring features just three pieces - the band of the ring, the gallery that mounts the gem, and then finally the gem itself.

With a few peripheral components such as earring-posts, chains, and hinges (often known as "findings"), these basic components are used to make everything from solitaire and gem-set rings, to earrings, necklaces, pendants and more complex pieces. While the Prong setting is the most frequently seen method of setting gems and Diamonds, there are a variety of other methods also used to set gems in precious metals.

Prong setting

Also known as the claw setting, the Prong setting has small metal prongs with a vise-like grip that are bent over the girdle of the gem to ensure its secure and enduring position. Typical Prong settings have 4 prongs. Prong settings with 6 prongs are also called the "Tiffany" setting because it was originally developed by the founder of Tiffany & Co. in 1886. Marquise and Trilliant cut gems can respectively have just 2 or 3 prongs at the corners where the points of the jewels are nestled in specialized v-shaped prongs (usually called "chevron prongs").

While the prongs must always be equal, the visible ends can be round shapes, oval shapes, points, chevrons, flats, and sometimes even formed into ornamental shapes (usually called "enhanced prongs").

As all gemstones are suitable for Prong setting, it is the most frequently used method of setting gems into jewelry. This is because the prongs are easier to adjust to the size of an individual gemstone. Understandably, the more prongs, the more secure and safe your gemstones will be.

Since the gemstone is positioned higher and is more easily seen, Prong setting brilliantly shows off the gemstone. Prong setting is especially popular for solitaire engagement rings and in bridal rings. When combined with Pave setting, Prong settings are considered to be the most suitable for designs with smaller shoulders or smaller gemstones.

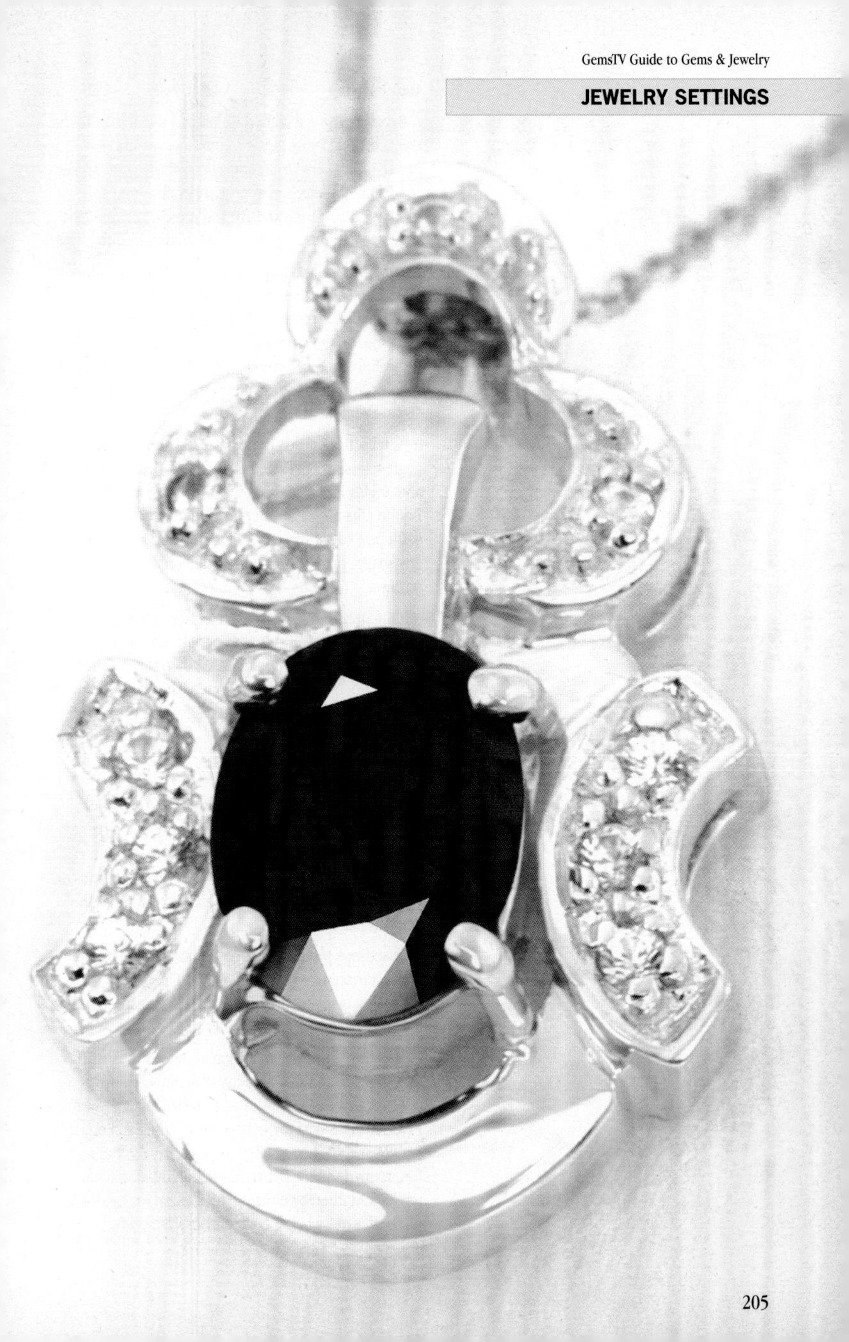

JEWELRY SETTINGS

Pave Setting

Channel Setting

Bezel setting

A Bezel setting is a crafted diskette of metal that holds the gemstone by its girdle to the ring, securely encircling the entire circumference of the gem. An age-old technique that can appear very contoured and modern, it is labor intensive and must be crafted to precisely circumnavigate the outline of the gem.

A variation of the Bezel setting is the "Flush" setting, where the surface of the ring has a window cut into it that exactly fits the size of the gem. Secured from underneath, the crown of the gem rises from the ring, beautifully catching rays of light. When the setting half surrounds the gemstone it is called a "Half-Bezel" or "Semi-Bezel" setting.

A Bezel setting needs to be balanced and straight, from angle-to-angle. Bezel setting gemstones cut with sides and angles is considered difficult, while Oval and Round cuts are easier. Bezels can have straight or scalloped edges and can be molded into a gemstone of any shape, protecting the gemstone's edges, girdle and pavilion.

Adding height, dimension and a great modern look, Bezel setting is well suited to people with active lifestyles. Bezel settings are ideal when the design has big shoulders or larger gemstones. The Bezel setting is best for earrings, necklaces, bracelets and rings.

Pave setting

Pronounced "pa-vay," Pave setting is a prong-like setting where the prongs are so small they are barely visible. The settings are created by the use of tiny handmade prongs that hold the gems on both sides or by scooping beads of precious metal out to hold the gems in place.

Pave settings produce a carpet of brilliance across the entire surface of a piece of jewelry. The surface is encrusted or quite literally "paved" in gems, vibrantly bringing the body of the jewelry to life.

Pave setting displays an illusionary bigger look using multiple gemstones and is usually combined with other gemstone settings to add more effect and beauty. Pave setting is best for Round, Oval, Princess, Emerald, Square and Baguette cut gemstones. Pave settings are frequently used for Diamonds in conjunction with white gold, thereby creating the illusion of the whole piece of jewelry being crafted from Diamonds.

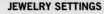

Channel setting

Channel setting is a technique whereby gemstones are set side-by-side with their girdles held between two long tracks of precious metal. When used with Square, Princess and Rectangular shaped gems the effect is breathtaking, as no metal appears between them. The gems appear to float in a tightly bejeweled chain within the jewelry.

The gemstones in Channel settings are set so closely together that no precious metal between the gems is necessary. This allows the set gems to display their maximum amount of brilliance. Understandably, it is very important that gemstones with precisely cut pavilions are used in Channel setting. If not, the gemstones will crack during setting or be later lost. Often seen in eternity band rings and tennis bracelets, Channel setting is increasingly common in modern jewelry designs featuring Round, Oval, Princess, Emerald, Square and Baguette cut gems.

Bar setting

Bar settings are constructed from short bars that run like a railway track across the jewelry. Gemstones are individually set between these bars leaving the sides of the gemstones exposed to light. An increasingly popular setting style, this technique maximizes the amount of light entering the gemstones thereby optimizing brilliance and sparkle. The Bar setting is a version of the Channel setting and can often combine a contemporary and classic look in one design. Bar setting is best for rings featuring Round, Oval, Princess, Emerald, Square and Baguette cut gems.

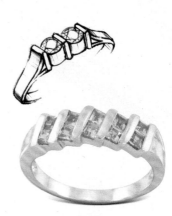

Bar Setting

From left to right, Tanzanite solitaires in Prong, Bar and Semi-Bezel settings

PRECIOUS METALS

Gold

Long considered the most precious of metals, gold is deeply woven into the very fabric of human culture. It captures our imagination and has inspired numerous legends and myths throughout the course of history. Gold has been treasured, hoarded, coveted and lavishly bestowed upon people, temples and objects of worship. Responsible for creating global currencies, starting wars, toppling empires, mass migrations and more, gold has helped shaped the course of human history - it is a metal that we are inextricably bound to.

Untarnishable, incorrodible, it is the most malleable of metals, yet remains miraculously strong. While its rich luster has long influenced the affairs of state and religion, its primary use remains within the realms of personal adornment.

Frequently featuring as an integral part of antique and modern jewelry's numerous forms, purchasers should be aware of what gold varieties are on offer and why. The following will shed some light on this ancient metal's application in today's market place.

Gold purity

Pure gold is relatively soft and as a consequence has durability problems. Ornate pieces of jewelry can be bent, and expensive gemstones can be lost from their settings. This unacceptable tendency of pure gold has largely given rise to the modern gold we find in the jeweler's window today.

Virtually all gold featured in jewelry today is alloyed with secondary metals that enhance its everyday durability. These gold alloys are so frequent, that in many countries many people find the color of pure gold peculiar! However, not all gold purities are the same. The different purities of gold alloys used by jewelers give consumers varying options regarding gold color, affordability and durability.

Gold purity is measured in karats. While the term "karat" may sound identical to the term "carat," which is used to measure weight in gemstones, the two terms do not have the same meaning. Karat ratio in gold tells you the percentage or proportion of gold purity. Gold with a higher karat ratio is comparatively more expensive gram for gram when compared to gold with lower karat ratios. Expressed as a ratio of 24 parts, the most frequently seen gold purities are:

22 Karat: 91.6% Pure Gold

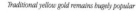
Traditional yellow gold remains hugely popular

18 Karat: 75.0% Pure Gold
14 Karat: 58.5% Pure Gold
10 Karat: 41.7% Pure Gold

Gold pricing

Raw, un-worked gold pricing is based on the karat ratio and the gold weight. For jewelry, we must also take into account additional factors. Diamonds and gemstones must be accounted for, as well as construction techniques that can make a piece of jewelry more durable, more ornate, or even unique. Features such as robust clasps all add to the price of a piece of finished jewelry.

14K Yellow Gold

Gold sources

Gold is mined in several countries around the globe, but in terms of output, the main sources are South Africa, US, Australia, Canada, China, Russia, Peru and Indonesia.

Gold as an investment

Due to the popularity of gold, it has been used to both purchase and exchange goods for thousands of years. Until the early 1900s, gold reserves formed the basis of the world monetary systems. Even today, a huge proportion of the world's gold is held in government reserves. When you purchase gold jewelry, although you are not guaranteed that you will ever make a profit on your acquisition, you are assured that you have gained something with an intrinsic value.

14K White Gold

Gold colors

Gold comes in a number of different colors offering consumers a wide choice when buying this lustrous precious metal:

Yellow gold: Displaying a timeless color, this is the most frequently seen gold type. It is alloyed with silver and copper.

White gold: White gold can be alloyed white (i.e., pure gold is yellow) with silver, palladium (a precious platinum group metal) or nickel. Most white gold jewelry is also rhodium plated. Rhodium is the most expensive platinum group precious metal (approximately 3 times more expensive than

14K Rose Gold

PRECIOUS METALS

platinum) and provides a hard, brilliant finish that is unmatched by any other metal. Our rhodium is electroplated and will last 2-3 years with normal wear. However, it is also white underneath, creating true white gold jewelry.

Rose gold: Alloyed with copper, this increasingly popular gold type has a striking pinkish rose color.

Gold types

While solid gold is the most frequently seen gold type available in the market, buyers should also be aware of the other gold types available, which deliver comparable beauty at different values. Naturally, the higher the gold proportions or weight, the more expensive they are:

Gold filled: Also known as gold overlay. This term refers to a gold layer that has been bonded to a support metal. To qualify for use of this term, the gold must be at least 10% of the total weight.

Gold plate: Means that a thin layer of gold plating has been bonded to a base metal.

Vermeil: Pronounced "vur-may," this process derives from the French word for "veneer." It is also known as onlay, double or silver gilt. It is typically a combination of sterling silver and gold. To be considered vermeil, the gold must also be at least 10 Karat and 1.5 micrometers (or greater) in thickness. The original fire-gilding process was developed in France in the 18th century, but today vermeil is mainly produced by electrolysis. The White House has a collection of vermeil tableware kept appropriately in the Vermeil Room.

Gold leaf: Ultra-thin gold plating that's pounded and thinned, then applied to an object.

Citrine Yellow 14K Gold Pendant

Silver

With a rich history stretching back some 5,000 years, like gold, silver occupies a hallowed place in our collective history. From the age-old Sumerian city of Ur, to the ancient Americas, to Greco-Roman culture and the ancient Far East, silver has been used by nearly all global cultures over the last two millennia.

Sharing much in common with its more glamorous counterpart gold, silver too is most frequently used for personal adornment.

Carnelian 925 Silver Bracelet

Silver purity

Like gold, pure silver or fine silver is relatively soft and malleable. As a result, painstakingly crafted jewelry and other objects can be easily damaged if created from pure silver. As a consequence, silver is commonly alloyed with secondary metals, usually copper, to create a more durable precious metal.

Sterling Silver is the standard for beautiful high-quality silver jewelry and other objects d'art. It's 92.5% pure silver, and is alloyed with secondary metals for added strength and durability. Unlike gold, but like platinum, silver purities are expressed as units of 1,000 parts. The most regularly seen silver purities are:

958: 95.8% Pure Silver, also known as Britannia Silver

925: 92.5% Pure Silver, also known as Sterling Silver

Silver pricing

The small amount of copper added to sterling silver has little effect on the value. Instead, the price of silver items is affected by the labor and craftsmanship involved in finishing an item.

Platinum

Sixty times rarer than gold, platinum is only found in a few locations worldwide - Russia's Ural Mountains, South Africa's Merensky Reef and a few small mines in the US and Canada. Relatively new to the jewelry market, platinum is fast becoming incredibly popular and is already a bedrock of the contemporary jewelry landscape. Purer, stronger and denser than gold, platinum is considered by many to be the ultimate and most luxurious of all precious metals.

Platinum Purity

Platinum purity is expressed differently than gold. Instead of expressing purity in ratios of 24 parts, platinum standards are expressed as units of 1,000 parts.

The most regular platinum purities seen are:

950: 95% Pure Platinum

900: 90% Pure Platinum

850: 85% Pure Platinum

Amethyst & Marcasite 925 Silver Pendant

PRECIOUS METALS

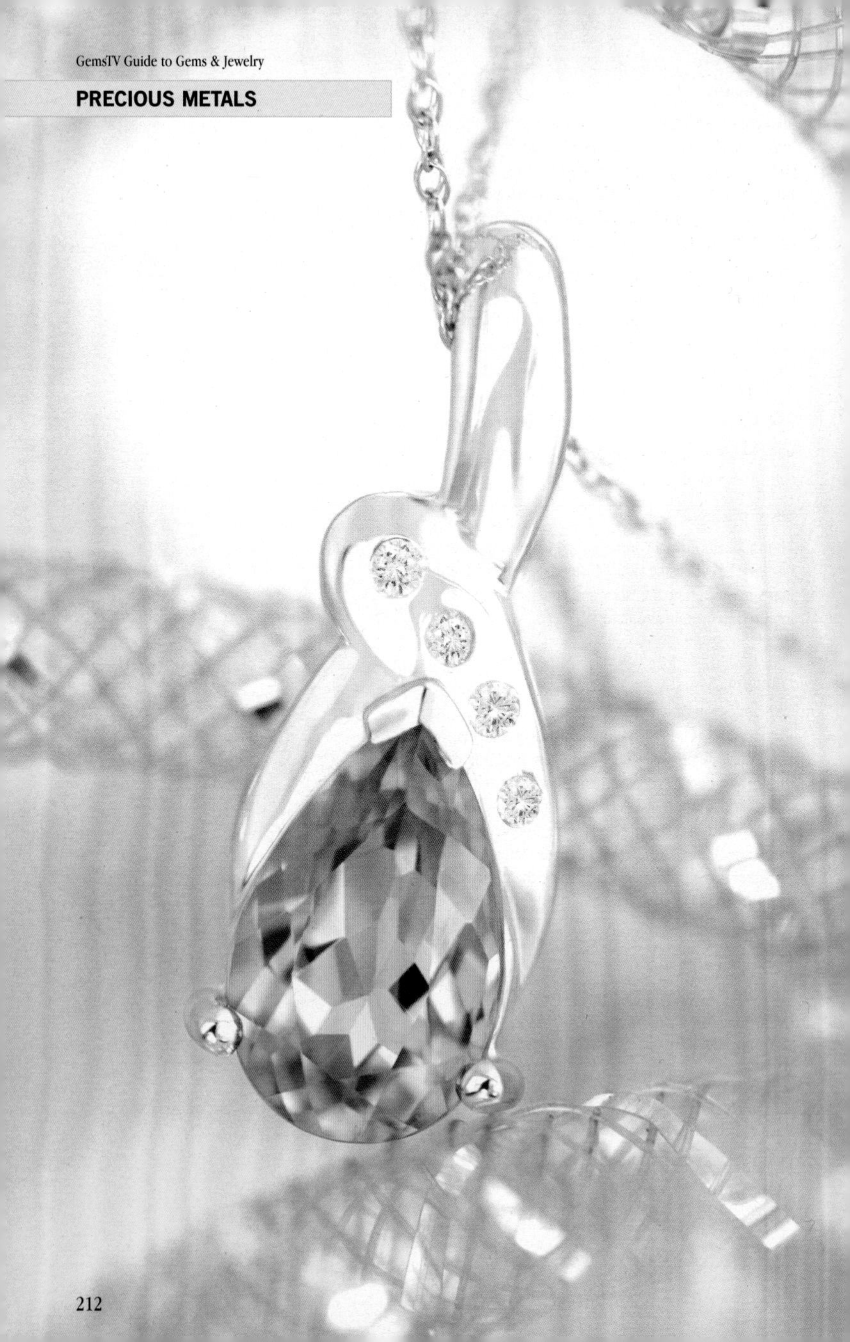

Troy Ounce

Precious metals such as gold and silver are often sold by the Troy Ounce. Many people don't realize that an ounce of gold is about 10% more than the typical ounce found at the grocery store. It is thought that the Troy Ounce was named after a weight system used in Troyes, France during the Middle Ages. One Troy Ounce weighs 31.10 grams.

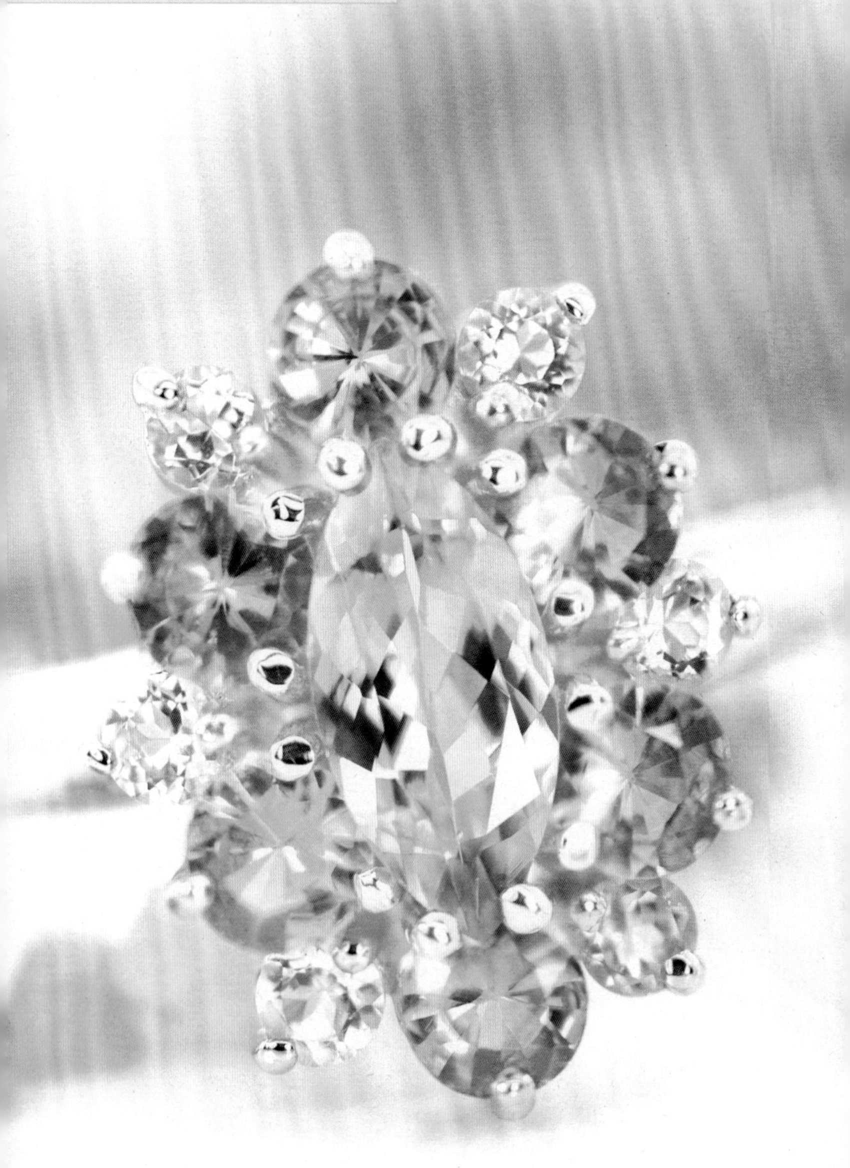

JEWELRY APPRAISALS

As you will probably want to insure the jewelry you purchase from GemsTV for the cost of replacement, this means seeking an independent appraisal from an experienced professional. Before seeking third-party appraisals, please take the following into consideration:

Insuring jewelry

Don't assume that your jewelry collection is automatically insured by your household policy. Furthermore, it is always wise to take photos and catalog all of your jewelry. Try and keep all your receipts and retain as many written details as possible (e.g., our certificates of authenticity). If your catalog is a hard copy, make sure you take a photocopy and keep the second copy at a friend's house or as some collectors do, leave a copy with your family lawyer. If your catalog is a soft copy on your personal computer, make a copy of the data and keep it in a different location.

Valuation

An appraisal valuation is what someone is prepared to pay for something. For example, what is the value of the Mona Lisa? Is the value the same as the cost of the canvas and the paint or is it determined by the amount that someone will pay for it? We believe that jewelry appraisals should reflect the average cost you would have to pay to replace the item if lost or stolen.

Independent

On these pages are just some of the thousands of comments we have received from delighted customers whose appraisals have exceeded their expectations. Unfortunately, we have also heard that some customers have had a negative experience when obtaining appraisals from local jewelers. As GemsTV is an integrated manufacturer and television home shopping retailer of colored gemstone jewelry, we cut out numerous middlemen. This keeps our prices extremely competitive. While most jewelers thank us for increasing the awareness of colored gems, a few may feel threatened and try to discredit our jewelry. Please bear this in mind when seeking appraisals.

"When I first found GemsTV I was very skeptical and ordered an inexpensive pendant. When it arrived, I was totally impressed and my addiction began. Since then, I have purchased numerous items and became confident enough to order more expensive jewelry.

I had no knowledge of Paraiba Tourmaline and ordered a 3.14 carat ring for $799. I was overwhelmed when I received the appraisal for $7,250. I now have a Paraiba obsession and purchased another ring for $1,570 that appraised for $9,800 and a pendant for $589 that appraised for $3,400.

Not only have I found that I can order with absolute confidence in the quality and return policies, but the entire staff from presenters to phone operators are exceptional."

Jean from Virginia

"I just thought I would drop you a line to tell you that the 3.65 carat AAA Tanzanite ring I just got is the most beautiful Tanzanite gem I have seen and I've seen a lot.

I took it to a very well known jeweler and he said it was a spectacular gem. He said the gem alone is worth at least $4,500 and that it was a well made piece of jewelry. I paid $2,700 for the 18K AAA Tanzanite & Diamond Gold Ring. Wow, that made my day! Keep up the good work."

Carolyn from California

JEWELRY APPRAISALS

"I am a regular viewer of GemsTV and have purchased many beautiful items. I currently have over five Paraiba rings and two Paraiba pendants from GemsTV. All these items have been appraised for much more than I bought them for and I am continuing to add to my collection. Thanks again for brining such amazing jewelry at more amazing prices. I love it!"

Lisa from Michigan

"I purchased from GemsTV a 1.3 carat 18K Majestic Ruby & Diamond White Gold Ring for $399. When I received the ring, I was very pleasantly surprised by the color of the gem. When taking one of my husband's rings to be re-sized, I asked what it might cost to have a pendant made to match my ring. The jeweler looked at the ring, got out his loupe, and said that it had been years since he had seen a ruby of such color and quality, and that if he could find one, his cost would be at least $2,000. That didn't include the 18K gold or accent Diamonds. It is a beautiful ring that is commented upon wherever I wear it. Thank you, GemsTV."

Connie from Illinois

Knowledge

Although most appraisers will have experience valuing gold, silver and Diamonds, some may not have even heard of some of the gemstones offered by GemsTV. When obtaining an appraisal it's always a good idea to confirm that the appraiser possesses the requisite experience to value colored gemstone jewelry. This can be easily determined by asking if they have received any formal gemology training. As visual inspection is not a reliable means of identifying gemstones, please make sure you ask what tools (e.g., refractometer, jeweler's loupe, etc.) they used to perform their appraisal.

One question we are routinely asked is how appraisers can know the weight of gemstones without removing them from their settings? If you pick up two different gem types of the same size and shape you may notice that one feels heavier than the other. This is due to differences in their chemical composition and crystal structure resulting in some gem types being denser than others. While "Specific Gravity" (i.e., the ratio of the weight of a specific material to the weight of the same volume of water) was used as the index to measure the density of gemstones this is now largely replaced by "Relative Density," which is expressed as grams per cubic centimeters on a 1 to 8 scale. Given this, an appraiser will measure the set gem with calipers, and then based on their knowledge, extrapolate an estimate. For example, a 7x5 millimeter Oval-cut Sapphire weighs approximately 1 carat, a 7x5 millimeter Oval-cut Topaz weighs approximately 0.70 to 0.80 carats and a 7x5 millimeter Oval-cut Zircon weighs approximately 1.20 to 1.50 carats. However, these are estimates only. The only accurate way to measure carat weight is to remove the gem from its setting and weigh it. As this should be avoided, we include the MTGW (Minimum Total Gem Weight) on our certificates of authenticity.

BIRTHSTONES

GemsTV use the official birthstones established by the American National Association of Jewelers in 1912 and revised in 2002. Most experts agree that birthstones became part of western culture through the Breastplate of Aaron (Exodus 28:15-30).

January

Garnet

February

Amethyst

March

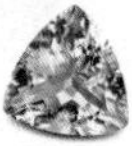

Aquamarine

April

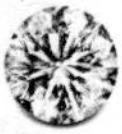

Diamond

May

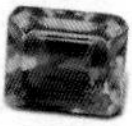

Emerald

June

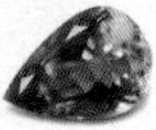

Alexandrite

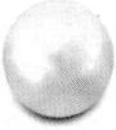

Pearl

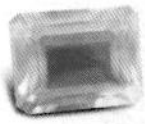

Moonstone

July

Ruby

August

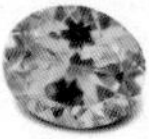

Peridot

September

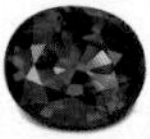

Sapphire

October

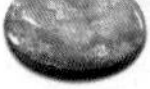

Opal

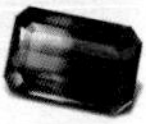

Tourmaline

November

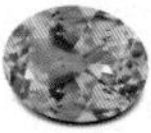

Topaz

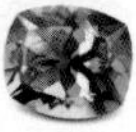

Citrine

December

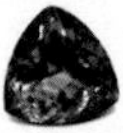

Tanzanite

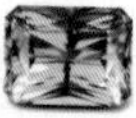

Zircon

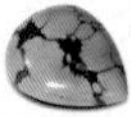

Turquoise

ANNIVERSARY GEMS

Although these gemstones are associated with wedding anniversaries, many people give them as gifts to celebrate all kinds of anniversaries.

1st
Gold Jewelry

2nd
Garnet

3rd
Pearls

4th
Blue Topaz

5th
Sapphire

6th
Amethyst

7th
Onyx

8th
Tourmaline

9th
Lapis Lazuli

10th
Diamond Jewelry

11th
Turquoise

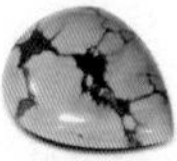

12th
Jade

14th
Opal

15th
Ruby

16th
Peridot

17th
Amethyst

18th
Cat's Eye Beryl

19th
Garnet

20th
Emerald

21st
Iolite

22nd
Spinel

23rd
Imperial Topaz

24th
Tanzanite

25th
Silver Jubilee

30th
Pearl Jubilee

35th
Emerald

39th
Cat's Eye

40th
Ruby

45th
Sapphire

50th
Golden Jubilee

52nd
Star Ruby

55th
Alexandrite

60th
Diamond Jubilee

65th
Star Sapphire

70th
Sapphire Jubilee

75th
Diamond

Originating in ancient India, below is a correlation of gems with the astrological signs of the zodiac.

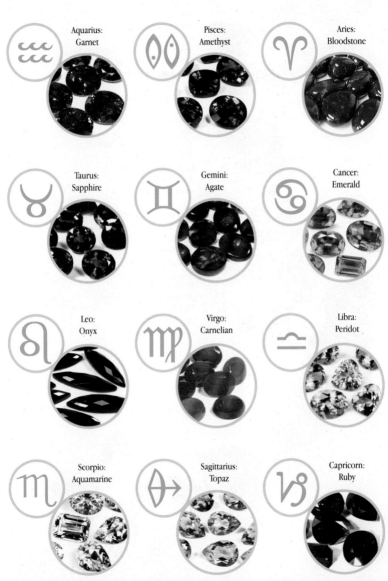

Aquarius:
Garnet

Pisces:
Amethyst

Aries:
Bloodstone

Taurus:
Sapphire

Gemini:
Agate

Cancer:
Emerald

Leo:
Onyx

Virgo:
Carnelian

Libra:
Peridot

Scorpio:
Aquamarine

Sagittarius:
Topaz

Capricorn:
Ruby

USEFUL CONTACTS

AGTA Gemological Testing Center
18 East 48th Street, Suite 502
New York, NY 10017
Tel: 212-752-1717
www.agta-gtc.org

American Gemological Laboratories
580 Fifth Avenue, Suite 706
New York, NY 10036
Tel: 212-706-0727
www.aglgemlab.com

Gemological Institute of America (GIA)
World Headquarters
The Robert Mouawad Campus
5345 Armada Drive
Carlsbad, California 92008
Tel: 800-421-7250
www.gia.edu

International Colored Gemstone Association
19 West 21st Street, Suite 705
New York, NY 10010-6805
Tel: 212-620-0900
www.gemstone.org

Jewelers of America
52 Vanderbilt Ave, 19th Floor
New York, NY 10017
Tel: 800-223-0673
www.jewelers.org

INDEX

ACKNOWLEDGMENTS

The author and GemsTV would like to thank the following people for their contribution to this guide:

Alex Sharp, Carolyn Perkins, Chris Vernell, Dave Rick, Debby Cavill, Don Kogen, Dylan Bartlett, Emma Jeffares, Hathaichanok Malee, Jo Wheeler, Lee Roberts, Mary Baladad, Matthew McNamara, Michelle Duggins, Mitsunari Yoshimoto, Narumon Tongkom, Praniti Sonsa and Steve Ashton.

In addition, we thank all GemsTV employees globally and extend our kindest appreciation to all our valued customers, especially those who have permitted their appraisals to be published in this guide.

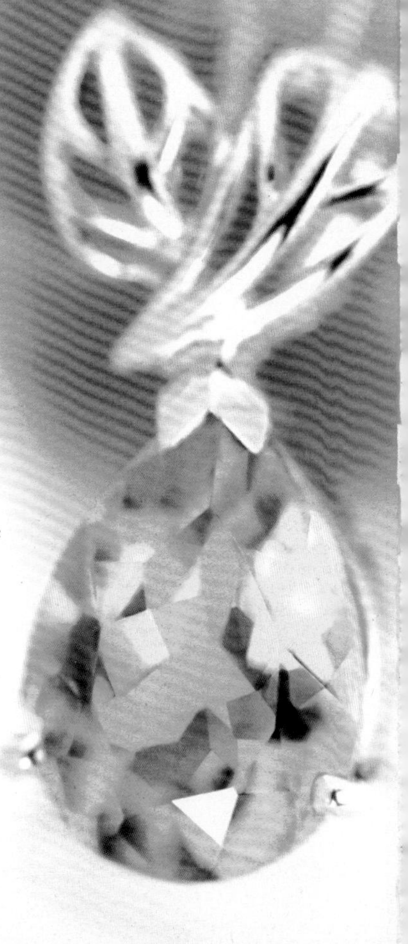

About the author

Gavin Linsell's love affair with gems started under the shadow of the jungle-clad vistas of Khao Ploi Waen "The Mountain of Gemstone Rings" located in Chanthaburi, Thailand, an international center for colored gemstones. Gavin has lived in Chanthaburi for eight years.

Combining an infectious enthusiasm for gemstones with a background in marketing, Gavin suffers when hearing gemstones called "stones" or synthetics marketed as "gems." He is dedicated to gemstones formed within the earth, not a laboratory.

Australian by birth, Gavin lives in Thailand with Natasha and their four dogs. He attributes his best qualities to his parents, a travel bug and his keen gemstone quality eyesight!